THE CHURCHES AND MENTAL HEALTH

Joint Commission
on Mental Illness and Health

MONOGRAPH SERIES / NO. 8

The Churches and Mental Health

RICHARD V. MCCANN

A REPORT TO THE STAFF DIRECTOR, JACK R. EWALT

1962

Basic Books, Inc., Publishers, New York

© 1962 BY BASIC BOOKS PUBLISHING CO., INC.

LIBRARY OF CONGRESS CATALOG CARD NUMBER: 62–11204

MANUFACTURED IN THE UNITED STATES OF AMERICA

Foreword

THIS IS the eighth of a series of monographs to be published by the Joint Commission on Mental Illness and Health as part of a national mental health survey culminating in *Action for Mental Health,* the final report containing findings and recommendations for a national mental health program (Basic Books, 1961. $6.75).

The present document constitutes a report of the project director to the staff director of the Joint Commission.

Titles of the monograph series, together with the principal authors, are listed here in the order of publication:

1. *Current Concepts of Positive Mental Health*
   Marie Jahoda, Ph.D., Basic Books, 1958. $2.75.

2. *Economics of Mental Illness*
   Rashi Fein, Ph.D., Basic Books, 1958. $3.00.

3. *Mental Health Manpower Trends*
   George W. Albee, Ph.D., Basic Books, 1959. $6.75.

4. *Americans View Their Mental Health. A Nationwide Interview Survey*
   Gerald Gurin, Ph.D., Joseph Veroff, Ph.D., and Sheila Feld, Ph.D., Survey Research Center, University of Michigan, Basic Books, 1960. $7.50.

5. *Community Resources in Mental Health*
   Reginald Robinson, Ph.D., David F. DeMarche, Ph.D., and Mildred K. Wagle, M.S.S.A., Basic Books, 1960. $8.50.

6. *Epidemiology and Mental Illness*
   Richard J. Plunkett, M.D., and John E. Gordon, M.D., Basic Books, 1960. $2.75.

These monographs, each a part of an over-all study design, contain the detailed information forming the basis of the final report. The Staff Review found in previous monographs has been omitted from the present work inasmuch as the material has been incorporated in *Action for Mental Health*. A short review of *The Churches and Mental Health* may be found there.

Participating organizations, members and officers of the Joint Commission and the headquarters staff are listed in an appendix at the end of this book.

The Joint Commission, it may be seen, is a nongovernmental, multidisciplinary, nonprofit organization representing a variety of national agencies concerned with mental health. Its study was authorized by a unanimous resolution of Congress and was financed by grants from the following sources:

American Association on Mental Deficiency
American Association of Psychiatric Clinics for Children
American Legion
American Medical Association
American Occupational Therapy Association
American Orthopsychiatric Association, Inc.
American Psychiatric Association
American Psychoanalytic Association
Association for Physical and Mental Rehabilitation
Carter Products Company
Catholic Hospital Association

Field Foundation
Henry Hornblower Fund
National Association for Mental Health
National Committee Against Mental Illness
National Institute of Mental Health
National League for Nursing
National Rehabilitation Association
Rockefeller Brothers Fund
Benjamin Rosenthal Foundation
Smith, Kline and French Foundation

Additional copies of *The Churches and Mental Health* may be purchased from the publisher or from book dealers.

JOINT COMMISSION ON MENTAL ILLNESS AND HEALTH

Acknowledgments

AMONG THE MANY individuals who contributed time and thought to this study, the author wishes especially to acknowledge the help of the following:

Nathan Altshuler, Ph.D., Research Associate on the project, strengthened the study in many ways. John Dickinson, Robert Christian, Gene Nameche, Berkeley Hathorne, Ellen Waldron, and Doris Butler contributed substantially to our study.

Warm thanks are extended to the panel of advisors to the project: Gordon W. Allport, Ph.D., the Reverend George C. Anderson, S.T.B., Kenneth E. Appel, M.D., Norman Birnbaum, Ph.D., Walter Houston Clark, Ph.D., William Douglas, Ph.D., Sol W. Ginsburg, M.D., Hans Hofmann, Th.D., Henry E. Kagan, Ph.D., D.D., Herbert C. Kelman, Ph.D., Bernice Moore, Ph.D., and the Reverend Alexius Portz, O.S.B.

Others who gave wise counsel are Walter E. Barton, M.D., and M. Brewster Smith, Ph.D., of the Joint Commission's Committee on the Studies; Charlotte Green Schwartz, M.A., Reginald Robinson, Ph.D., and Gerald Gurin, Ph.D., of the Joint Commission staff; and John M. Billinsky, Ed.D., Anton T. Boisen, D.D., Paul E. Johnson, Ph.D., and Henry A. Murray, M.D. Mrs. Jean Blumen, Drs. Allen Eister, J. E. Carlin, S. H. Mendlovitz, Jeshaia Schnitzer, and Luke M. Smith kindly gave permission to quote from published studies.

Contents

THE CHURCHES AND MENTAL HEALTH

I

Introduction

MORE THAN seventeen million Americans, it is estimated, suffer from some form of mental disorder (although fewer than 700,000 of them can be numbered in mental hospitals on any one day). It would appear that still more find their lives goal-less, without meaning or purpose, and seem to be ineffective to varying degrees, uncreative in their life and work, living on the edge of life. To these must be added yet others who experience, or are affected by, the varied by-products of mental disorders.

Over one hundred million Americans are members of churches and synagogues, and about 170,000,000—or 95 per cent of our total population—say they believe in God. The number of persons without diagnosable mental illness is high, and so is the number with some kind of religious commitment, whether in the form of belief, or membership in a religious body. Yet to claim that the vast majority of the populace are mentally healthy because they belong to a church or believe in God would no doubt be as extravagant as to claim that their health derives solely from their education, or from their membership in a democracy.

The United States now has the highest percentage of church members (60 per cent) in its history. Max Lerner (1957, p. 711) points out that while this growth in membership may represent some kind of "return to religion," what kind is not clear. "It could mean a new groping for faith as a compensation for the ugliness and danger of life. Or it might mean that in most American communities church membership is a badge of social status and that membership . . . represents safety in a conformist, church-going society."

[3]

The hundred million church members who are "groping for a faith" or seeking safety and status or simply worshipping God are the concern of approximately 235,000 clergymen of all faiths. The person and work of the clergy is one of the foci, one point at which religion and mental health intersect, clash, cooperate, or otherwise find mutual relevance. Other points of intersection are the theoretical ground between theology and psychiatry; the relation between the clergy and the psychiatrist and other mental health resources; the life, experience, problems, conflicts of the individual layman (and, often, of the individual clergyman as well).

While we are concerned with religious faith as a source of mental health or illness, and the relation between the total religious life and orientation and total health, in view of the fifteen months we had available for planning and carrying out this study we had to make a choice between the more manifest and the more latent, more subtle aspects of the topic. In choosing to deal with some of the more manifest aspects, as symbolized by the title, *The Churches and Mental Health,* among the things we most wanted to learn is what the church, as a potential mental health resource, and as represented primarily by its clergy, makes available to its members (and to non-members as well).

It is appropriate to consider here a few of the myriad implications of the terms *religion* and *mental health.*

There are as many definitions and criteria of mental health as of religion. The vast generalization, "mental health," can be approached in a number of ways. One is by enumerating, analyzing, and interrelating some of its components, which though more accessible still remain at a level of abstraction. Another is by attempting to understand what is meant by a mentally healthy person.

Mental health is not merely absence of mental illness, many authorities agree. Nor does it consist merely in freedom from all anxiety, conflict, and tension, nor merely in normality, nor only in adjustment. M. Brewster Smith (1959, p. 673) points to some of the complexities of the concept and the difficulties of dealing with it: "We may regard a Khrushchev as mentally healthy at the same time we judge him to be socially destructive; a Dostoevski may be mentally ill yet artistically creative. Mental health, thus viewed, is complex and not easily schematized. It is a cluster of values that compete with other values in the arena of personal and social choice. We will not always want to give it priority."

Marie Jahoda (1958) has distinguished basic criteria for positive mental health. We paraphrase her concepts to apply them to the "mentally healthy individual":

1. He is self-reliant, self-confident and self-accepting.

2. His degree of self-actualization is such that his motivational processes can be characterized as growth motivation rather than need motivation.

3. He can resist stress, has a unifying outlook on life, and his psychic forces are in flexible balance; that is, he shows a relatively good integration of the personality.

4. He is autonomous (rather than, in Riesman's terms, either "adjusted" on the one hand or "anomic" on the other). He maintains a stable set of internal standards for his actions, so that he is relatively independent of social influences.

5. He is able to perceive the world and other persons with relative freedom from the distortions that may originate in his own needs. Related to this perception of reality is empathy, or social sensitivity, by virtue of which he will treat the inner life of others as a matter worthy of his concern.

6. He is adapted to his environment, displaying a creative capacity for love, work, and play.

The Rev. Harry C. Meserve (1958), Program Director of the Academy of Religion and Mental Health, delineates ten characteristics that might be associated with mental health and with "a sound religious point of view," forming a kind of profile of the "healthy religious person."

1. The healthy religious person has found a framework of meaning, both theological and humanistic, within which he is able to

judge and evaluate the more specific meanings and choices of his own life.

2. He is in touch with reality, and has come to see that growth or improvement in himself or others or the world cannot come into being except from the condition of things as they are.

3. He makes a fetish neither of conformity nor of nonconformity, but guards his own integrity and freedom of judgment.

4. He sees life as a journey from the known and familiar to the unknown and the new.

5. He finds peace of mind (though "only the discontented may inherit content") and refreshment of spirit in the work he has undertaken, and in the companionship of kindred souls in the religious community whose struggles and adventures he shares.

6. He has a realistic attitude toward the tribulations of the world. He knows that not all his dreams can come true and that suffering is an inevitable part of life and growth, since man is both mortal and fallible.

7. His approach to the world and to the people around him is expectant and hopeful, rather than critical and negative.

8. He has achieved within himself a sound working balance between self-criticism and self-confidence (rather than being oriented wholly toward the former, as in some Christian traditions). He knows that he shares in the sin and corruption that are part of the human condition, but dares to affirm his own worth.

9. He has developed a capacity for enjoyment of the world and its people.

10. Most of all, he has learned how to give himself to something that is worth loving and serving, and in so doing, has found a new self with greater resources and deeper insights than the old. Mental and religious health consist in being needed and being in some measure able to meet the need.

In addition to the healthy religious person, a profile could no doubt be sketched for the healthy unreligious person, the unhealthy religious person, and the unhealthy unreligious person. Which of these would preponderate in our culture is impossible to estimate.

We do not know, for example, whether the hundred million and more church members or the 170,000,000 "believers" are mentally healthy, or even whether they are religious.

Church membership or affiliation is, of course, only one aspect of religiousness, and probably not the determining one. Belief in a Supreme Being would seem to be a more central factor in the religious life, yet it too is only one of many aspects of an individual's religion, and the relation between belief and mental health is difficult to assess. In a study of the Hutterites, an economically communal anabaptist sect in the western part of the United States and Canada, Joseph W. Eaton and Robert J. Weil (1955, p. 217) found that "formal religious affiliations are not important for personality dynamics but strongly held faiths are. From the therapeutic point of view religion can be both a positive and a negative mental health element. It gives many Hutterites a sense of great security but is also responsible for the high frequency of guilt feelings."

Religious affiliation and faith are only two of many values that constitute the individual's religious life. Margaret Mead has called mental health a "moving target"; religion too is a moving target, as an object of our understanding, as an achievement of the individual life, and in its diverse manifestations as cultural phenomena and individual expressions.

The diverse forms religion takes in the culture, in the society, have been subjected to the scrutiny of countless competent critics. Max Weber discerned alternative types of the religious group, distinguishing between the voluntary "submission" which characterizes the "sect" and the authoritarian moral discipline characteristic of the "church." Auguste Sabatier distinguished "religions of authority" from the "religion of the spirit." The former are characterized by a legalistic, authoritarian approach to theology, according to which only divine intervention will bring about an ideal world; the religion of the spirit recognizes an evolutionary growth reinforced by social pressures and techniques. Ernst Troeltsch, J. Milton Yinger, and others have described the "sect-type" and "church-type," and their variations and alternatives.

Yet, few attempts have been made to learn who the adherents of such contrasting religious groups are, what are their personality characteristics, and why these adherents are appealed to by the manifest—and latent—values of each religious group. No explorations have been made of the whole religious constellation of the individual—his religious beliefs, sentiments, behavior, experience—and their relation to his life, his effectiveness, his creativity, his "degree" of mental health. Most empirical studies of religion have been limited to one variable, particularly to "religious experience" in the narrow use of that term. As late as the first quarter of the twentieth century a "religious experience" was thought to be the sine qua non of the religious life. This interpretation of "true religion" was reflected in the insistent emphasis on conversion and mysticism seen in almost all empirical studies of religion.

What is probably the earliest empirical study of religion in the United States—and, in some respects, an exception to the trend noted above—is Jonathan Edwards' *Treatise on the Religious Affections*. Published in 1746, it was based on first-hand observation of his parishioners. The important question to Edwards was, "What are the distinguishing qualifications of those in favor with God; that is, what is the nature of true religion, and in what does holiness consist?" He considered Grace to be "the work of God in which He communicates the holiness of His nature"; and the proof of that Grace was found in a change in the nature of the individual, its fruit being "exercises in Christian practice." For Edwards, the "religious affections" were "the emotions and sentiments of the religious life." "Religion," he concludes, "consists much in holy affection; but those exercises of affection which are most characteristic of true Religion are practical exercises."

Edwards seems to be very sophisticated for his time when we consider his sensitivity to the relation between the religious experience and the religious life, between the sacred and the secular, and his awareness of the need to "de-compartmentalize" both; but hardly more so than, for example, St. Augustine, as reflected in his *Confessions* a millennium before.

Between Edwards' time and the turn of the twentieth century many scholars gave their attention to the "Great Awakening" and subsequent religious revivals. Their work consisted largely of description and analysis of personal confessions and eyewitness accounts, and has long since been covered by the dust of time.

At the beginning of this century, James Starbuck investigated the social and biological aspects of conversion, which he termed an "unselfing" process; the physiological aspects related to "psychic awakening," and the psychological aspects of the process from what he calls the "fractured self" through the stage of intensification, to eventual harmony.

William James made use of much of Starbuck's collected material and of some of his concepts, deriving, for example, his ingenious and memorable typologies of the "once-born" and the "twice- born" from Starbuck's then revolutionary distinction between "religious development" and "religious conversion." James had no concern for the "second-hand religious life," or "your ordinary religious believer who follows the conventional observances," and hoped to find in the experience of "religious geniuses" clues to the kinds of religious experience which lay at the primitive root of our Christian tradition. As with Edwards, for whom the "fruits" of Grace and of religious experience were in "practical exercises," so for James the test of religious experience must be pragmatic, morally helpful. Yet his definition of religion—"the feelings, acts, and experiences of individuals in their solitude, so far as they apprehend themselves to stand in relation to whatever they may consider the divine"—would seem to discount not only the institutional and group aspects of religion, but also the religious follower, at second or third hand, whose spiritual life can sometimes be characterized by Robin Williams' phrase, "religion at a very low temperature."

Just as definitions, or characteristics and criteria, of the "healthy religious" person seem to be not too different from those of the "healthy" person, resemblances are found also in definitions of the "religious" person. Thus, definitions of religion, as well as some of the attributes and goals of religion, may be seen to resemble, at least in some measure, those of health.

Without attempting to summarize the definitions of religion and the religious person given by theologians, philosophers, and scientists, we select only a few that seem especially relevant to our study.

In contrast to William James' definition, Paul Tillich defines religion as "ultimate concern." Further, he sees religion not as revealing the nature of God—that is the content of revelation—but rather as man's *response* to that revelation.

For the religious man, according to Spranger, the highest value is unity. He seeks to comprehend the universe as a whole and to relate himself to its embracing totality. His "mental structure is permanently directed to the creation of the highest and absolutely satisfying value experiences."

Gordon W. Allport (1954) distinguishes two major types of religious orientation—the institutional or extrinsic, and the internalized, or intrinsic. For the "institutionalized" religious person, religion is likely to have only utilitarian value, and to be used in the service of his personal needs. He will depend on "the tribal investments of traditional religion for comfort and security." The person whose religion has been "internalized" has an inner sense of control and stability, rather than depending on props in the outside world as external control. He takes "the universalistic teachings of traditional religion as authentic guide to conduct." Rather than an "either-or" situation, both of the foregoing orientations may be present in the same individual, with one or the other predominating.

Effective internalization of religion, in Allport's sense of the term, may be the key to the harmonious integration of religious values and secular behavior. Once internalized, values are expressed —or, in a sense, re-externalized—in conduct, in relationships, in life situations. Many individuals have succeeded in making religion philosophically and ethically significant, so that it informs and infuses their personal life, pervading all areas of valuation, relationship, and choice. Many, on the other hand, have an immature form of religion which serves them as a mechanism for gratifying their needs for social identification, for clarification of role, for support. Although their religion may penetrate other areas of life, it does so in a utilitarian, supportive fashion. Even at a somewhat more sophisticated level of interpretation, religion often remains a device for achieving peace of mind, or personal adjustment, and thus remains more supportive than creative.

From the foregoing, we can derive a kind of "religious syndrome" that may serve to characterize some religious persons: (1) Belief in or orientation toward the highest unity, whether this is a personal God, the universe as a whole, or the "highest value experience"; (2) creative response to the object of such belief and orientation; (3) harmonious and effective internalization of religious values, and (4) realistic re-externalization of such values, expressed in the life of the individual.

Emil Brunner warns that the aim of religion is not to satisfy our wishes or to develop our personalities, but to realize the will of God. Many persons—perhaps most—"use" rather than "live" their religion. No doubt our vision is obscured, our sights are set too low, when we see religion only as a means to an end—such as contributing to the mental health of the individual as a goal. And to perceive the work of the church and of the clergy only as problem-oriented may be equally short-sighted.

But many people want to find solutions to their problems, or help in opening paths to the possibility of solution. And they look to their religion—to prayer, to their pastor, their church, their God—for help. Perhaps the ordinary citizen, for whom religion is a "dull habit" rather than an "acute fever," to use James's phrase, does not want to have an "ultimate concern." He does want comfort and happiness and success and "peace of mind," even though these may represent a low level of spiritual aspiration. It seems to be as naive to assume that most people are sophisticated religiously as it is to assume that the *only* function of religion in their lives is as a crutch, a device, a tool.

PART ONE

Church and Synagogue in Mental Health Endeavor

II

Ministering to the Mentally Ill

WHEN COMPARED with the quarter of a million clergymen of all faiths serving parishes, the four hundred mental hospital chaplains in this country may seem numerically insignificant. But they are no more insignificant than the 640,000 persons who make up our average daily mental hospital patient population, and who number over half (51 per cent) of all patients in all hospitals. It is to this population that the chaplain ministers. Because of his specialized training and the nature of his ministry, the chaplain illuminates and sharply highlights the church's concern and contributions in the area of mental illness and health. We begin our study of the churches and mental health, then, with consideration of the mental hospital chaplaincy.

The primary concern of the mental hospital chaplain is with persons who, because of a mental disorder severe enough to require hospitalization, have had to be separated from their homes, their jobs, their communities, for treatment, often for an extended period. Though the focus of the chaplain's work is in his relationship with patients, he is in a situation that may involve extensive and sometimes intensive cooperation with professional mental health workers.

In the community pastorate the clergyman must often deal with people under stress; but he works primarily with those who are able to function in their work and in their family life. The incidence of mental illness does vary from one community to another. Many factors are related to this variance. By chance or by choice, clergymen doing parish work will vary in their degree of contact with the mentally ill. Some, for example, serve inner-city churches in areas where the incidence—or visibility—of personal and social problems may be high. But whatever the variations, there is a great difference between the parish of the pastor in the "outside" community and the congregation to whom the mental hospital chaplain has chosen to minister. The chaplain's parishioners, through either voluntary or imposed commitment, are in the specialized community of the mental hospital, and they are there not primarily because they are religious but because they are ill.

It would be of interest to consider related types of chaplaincy, such as those in general hospitals and prisons; but we intend to limit this chapter to a consideration of the chaplaincy in the mental hospital. A discussion of the mental hospital chaplaincy would seem to be a fitting place to explore the relation of some religious factors to mental illness, such as aspects of religion that may be contributing causes of mental illness, and aspects that become part of the delusional systems of the mentally ill. It would be illuminating, for example, to review the work and explorations of such an experienced chaplain as Anton Boisen, who initiated specialized training programs for mental hospital chaplains thirty-five years ago, and who considers mental illness to be a problem-solving experience with deep religious implications. However, we will limit the scope of our inquiry to such aspects of the mental hospital chaplaincy as: how do chaplains prepare for their special ministry; what does their work entail; what are some of the chaplains' problems—with patient, staff, community. Our purpose is not to attempt a definitive statement about the chaplaincy, but rather to open up some areas of inquiry on the basis of our communications with many chaplains, with other members of hospital staffs, and with patients.

TRAINING FOR THE CHAPLAINCY

The chief aim of a mental hospital chaplain's training is a better pastoral ministry to patients. Everything else takes second place to this. Ernest Bruder (1957), Protestant chaplain at St. Elizabeths Hospital, Washington, D.C., notes:

Every profession working in the clinical situation recognizes that the academic training in the university situation is insufficient to provide the insights found in the "living human document" so essential to clinical treatment. The ministry can and must be no exception to this principle. The standards of the Council for Clinical Training, Inc., requiring at least one full year of clinical internship before a pastor can be fully accredited as a hospital chaplain, represent the minimum.

However, the ideal is so far removed from the actual situation that few departments of pastoral services of denominations and councils of churches insist on the full year requirement.

Where chaplain accreditation is demanded by a state, institution, or religious body, requirements of the National Conference on Clinical Pastoral Training are usually adopted. Additions are often made to these by the employer or religious group to which a chaplain is attached. An institution or state, for example, may specify the amount of previous pastoral or clinical experience which a candidate is to have. At least three years of ministerial experience and six months clinical internship are among the minimum requirements for the Protestant chaplaincy in Federal institutions, as set by the Department of Pastoral Services of the National Council of Churches.

While standards for the chaplaincy have been established, it is not known how many Protestant clergymen, appointed as chaplains before these standards were set up, now meet these requirements. Most Roman Catholic priests who become chaplains are assigned to a hospital after orientation but without specialized training; however, there are now seven centers for intensive training of Roman Catholic chaplains and chaplain-supervisors. Most Jewish chaplains serve on a part-time basis, principally owing to the comparatively low number of Jewish patients in state mental hospitals. Their primary source of formal training for the chaplaincy is through the Institute for Pastoral Psychiatry of the New York Board of Rabbis.

Although some religious groups fail to recognize the importance of clinical preparation for the chaplaincy, there is a growing awareness of this need. The Federation of Jewish Philanthropies of New York sponsors a chaplaincy training program and clears all appointments to state institutions through a Co-ordinator of Chaplaincies.

The Presbyterians, Lutherans, Baptists, Roman Catholics and other groups have taken a similar responsibility, following the course of those denominations affiliated with the Council for Clinical Training and the Institute of Pastoral Care.

The educational requirements for the chaplaincy are discussed in the chapter on clinical pastoral training. We shall describe here some programs whose chief aim is training for the institutional chaplaincy, rather than for the pastoral ministry in general.

At St. Elizabeths Hospital in Washington, D.C., the Protestant program, directed by Chaplain Bruder, is divided into two phases, for Chaplain Interns and Chaplain Residents. To qualify for the first, a candidate must have an undergraduate degree, a seminary degree, ordination, and some parish experience. The intern ministers to newly-admitted patients, both mentally and physically ill, and to patients whose problems are connected with religion. He conducts services and social and group activities, and consults with families, parish clergy, and staff members dealing with particular patients. He attends regular staff conferences, studies assigned reading, and takes part in community teaching programs on behalf of the hospital.

The Chaplain Resident expands his earlier clinical experience, doing some supervisory work himself, while still under the guidance of his Chaplain-Supervisor. St. Elizabeths aims to make the Chaplain Resident into a qualified teacher and supervisor of other clergymen. Most of those taking the intensive second year of training plan to be accredited as Chaplain-Supervisors, to teach pastoral theology in seminaries, or to specialize in pastoral counseling.

The chaplaincy training program at Hastings State Hospital, Minnesota, is under the direction of the Roman Catholic Chaplain, Father Joseph Quinlan. In addition to lectures, staff demonstrations, and seminars, the seminarian or clergyman in training gets experience in counseling, conducting services, visiting patients and families, and taking part in community activities. The program is a full year in length and is open to qualified clergymen and theological students of all faiths. It assumes that the hospital chaplain needs greater understanding of mental illness and psychiatric treatment than does the parish clergyman. The content of the course is accordingly designed to give the student some basic principles of psychiatry and mental health, in addition to continual work with patients, under supervision.

What does the chaplain's work actually consist of? A simple description of the chaplaincy program in St. Elizabeths Hospital, Washington, will provide a good example.

The administration of St. Elizabeths believe that patients should have the religious rights and privileges they have in the community. "Mental illness constantly involves the realm of faith and morals," says Chaplain Bruder, "and a great majority of patients have serious problems in this area which they find difficult to discuss." He notes the special value of the trained chaplain to a patient who fears that the psychiatrist may not understand his religious belief and devotion.

St. Elizabeths has a total of 7500 patients, of whom 4800 are Protestants, 1900 Roman Catholics, 200 Jews, 150 members of other faith groups, and 450 not attached to any faith. They are served by three full-time Protestant chaplains, two full-time Roman Catholic chaplains, and one part-time Jewish chaplain; the work of these men is further extended by the chaplains-in-training.

The Roman Catholic chaplains' work is in many respects similar to that of the parish priest. They celebrate six masses on Sundays and Holy Days in St. Elizabeths chapel. Confessions are heard in the chapel every Saturday, and in all wards once every five or six weeks. The chaplains, sometimes assisted by seminarians, conduct group discussions, counsel patients and their relatives, and recruit volunteers for various supplementary services, as well as for visiting and talking with patients. In a special report prepared in 1957, Father Wilbur F. Wheeler, Roman Catholic Supervisory Chaplain at St. Elizabeths, made an analysis of the Catholic chaplains' activities, finding that their various functions—particularly scheduled services, bedside and ward ministrations, ward visitation and counseling—required 207 hours per week.

The Jewish chaplain visits each newly-admitted Jewish patient, besides those included in his regular ward-visiting schedule. He holds a weekly service and special services for the High Holy Days and festivals.

The Protestant chaplains serve all other patients irrespective of denomination. There are regular services in six hospital buildings on Sundays and special holidays. Community clergymen are invited to hold services during Lent and Advent. Patients receive Communion in wards throughout the hospital at Christmas and Easter. As in the parish, patients are encouraged to take part in the religious program by ushering, singing in the choir, and the like.

The Protestant chaplains visit all newly-admitted patients and those they are requested to see by relatives, friends, community clergymen, and hospital staff members. Staff referrals, and less formal contacts as well, often lead to extended counseling relationships.

A part of the chaplains' obligation is considered to be carrying out an on-going program for educating the public in regard to mental health problems. The chaplains conduct short training and orientation programs for local clergymen, and take part in panel discussions, seminars, and other community programs in mental health, sometimes acting as consultants on mental health for church and civic groups. (Other aspects of the chaplains' educational activities will be discussed in connection with their part in clinical pastoral training programs.)

After description of a general nature, a view of the specific work of two state hospital chaplains may provide further perspective on the role of the chaplain. Chaplain D. is fifty-two years old, married, with three children. He has a Master's degree in theology, was a parish pastor for fifteen years, and had served as a part-time chaplain for six years prior to his present full-time appointment in a large hospital in a Western state. He is paid by the state on a regular civil service basis, receiving a salary of $557 per month.

Chaplain D. estimates that he spends 50 per cent of his time with patients and that, at present, he would know the names of at least 100. He visits new patients, makes ward rounds once every week, and does a follow-up on all patients who are transferred to other parts of the hospital. He conducts three ward services and one general service each week, the latter usually attended by about 300 patients. As a department head, Chaplain D. told us, he meets with doctors, the clinical director, the nursing director, the head of adjunctive therapies, the social service director, clinical psychologists, and is frequently called when he can help with a certain problem or patient. Chaplain D. is a member of the Council of Churches and also of the state's Committee on Chaplaincies. He works closely with local clergymen, and provides periodic workshops on mental health for both clergymen and laymen.

Chaplain M. serves the 600 Protestant patients in an 1800 bed state hospital in the Northeastern part of the country. The 1000 Roman Catholic patients are served by two priests who have their rectory in the hospital's Catholic chapel.

Chaplain M. was in business for twelve years before going to theological school. He has now spent several years in the ministry, and three summers in clinical pastoral training. He is thirty-nine years old and lives with his wife and two children in a town six miles from the hospital. Officially, he works a 30-hour week, the maximum provided for. To supplement his salary, he devotes ten hours a week to what he calls a "bed-side ministry" in a general hospital in a neighboring city.

Thursday—the day we followed Chaplain M. on his rounds—begins for the chaplain at 7:30 with Bible study for Protestant patients in the insulin ward. This lasts for about 30 minutes, between the time of the patients' injections and the onset of coma. The program, which was started at the request of the medical director of the insulin unit, allows the patients to study and discuss whatever they wish. Each patient takes part in the weekly discussions, which are not limited to the Bible but often touch on personal problems.

Services in wards in three parts of the hospital follow, from 8:30 to 11:00. A small choir and an organist (with a portable electric organ) accompany the chaplain. Usually, Gospel hymns, such as "Rock of Ages," are sung, since the patients seem to like these best. The ward services double as the choir's rehearsal for the following Sunday's services in the auditorium.

The chaplain visits with individual patients from 11:00 to 12:00 and after lunch holds a group session with Protestant men patients in the admissions building. This Thursday, 13 patients and a nurse took part. Chaplain M. let the patients take the lead in a desultory, half-joking way; but small talk, which occupied the first 15 minutes, was broken off when one patient accused the others of talking about everything but what really concerned them. The conversation then turned to the conflict between personal goals and social values, four patients, the chaplain, and a visitor taking an active part.

Immediately after this group, the chaplain holds a session with women patients (11 plus a nurse). The Roman Catholic nurse has been regularly attending these weekly sessions with the Protestant women patients for two years in order to know the patients better. On this particular day the patients talked about the clergy—in the home parish—as a source of help in time of trouble. One patient explained that, perhaps because of her experience of rejection by her stepfather, she could never go to her minister and never initiated talks with the chaplain. This prompted several patients to talk about their feelings about their parents and their clergymen.

The chaplain's day at the hospital ends with a "youth fellowship" from 4:00 to 5:00 P.M. held by the boys, girls, and nurses at the children's unit, a mile from the main grounds.

Friday, 8:15–9:45 A.M.: Rounds with the doctor on the Male Continued Treatment Service. The chaplain discusses patients, their progress and their problems with the doctor, occupational therapist, and social worker while visiting treatment rooms and seeing patients before electric shock treatments.

10:00–11:00 A.M.: Work in the children's unit. The chaplain gives religious instruction to Protestant patients while the Roman Catholic children are in catechism classes.

11:00 A.M.–3:00 P.M.: Visiting patients at the general hospital.

3:00–5:00 P.M.: Return to mental hospital for more visits with patients.

Saturday: Most of the day is spent at home preparing sermon and lessons for the coming week. The chaplain is on call for danger list cases.

Sunday, 8:15 A.M.: Children's service in the chapel of the children's unit. This is a regular worship service with Communion on the first

Sunday of the month, study of Biblical personages on the second, a service and sermon prepared by the children on the third, Bible doctrine on the fourth.

9:00 A.M.: Regular Sunday service for adults in the auditorium. Communion is served on the first Sunday, Bible personages studied on the second, hymns sung on the third, accompanied by stories of their origins, and Bible doctrine taught on the fourth.

10:15 A.M.: Visiting in wards. Chaplain M. discusses the service with patients, frequently relating it to the problem of a particular patient (relations with patients, getting jobs, attending the home church, facing the stigma of mental illness, or fear of clergy—which is often evident).

On an average, three out of every four Sunday evenings are occupied by speaking engagements.

Monday, 8:00–11:00 A.M.: Visiting new admissions.

12:00–3:00 P.M.: "Bed-side" ministry at the general hospital.

4:00–6:00 P.M.: Return to the state hospital for the same.

Tuesday: At home, except for danger list calls, a few of which usually come in. In the evening, Chaplain M. often has a speaking engagement. He explained that he accepts many requests to speak before church groups because he enjoys it, the Council of Churches expects it of a chaplain, and, although he never charges a fee, he often gets contributions to be used in his hospital work.

Wednesday: Schedule same as Monday's.

Chaplain M. told us that his chief problem is insufficient time and money to fulfill his many duties, while being sure of supporting his family at the same time. The state hospital has no fund for travel expenses or for such necessities as hymn books and prayer books, though sacramental equipment is paid for. The terms of Chaplain M.'s employment provide for no paid vacation, employee benefits, insurance, housing, or car expenses. In all mental institutions of the state in which he works, chaplains have the status of "consultants," and are not officially hospital staff members, though in some hospitals they may be considered an *ex officio* part of the staff.

The maintenance of relationships with patients, staff, and community requires constant planning and work. Chaplain M. considers it his responsibility to help to bring the laity to a better understanding of mental illness. This, he believes, will prevent their turning away from the mentally ill and may encourage their cooperation in the parish. Of staff relationships, he says, "If anything seems to be difficult, I go directly to the person and iron it out. I have had enough experience in business and in clinical training to know what my role is. I think I've defined my role: I'm a minister and a chaplain."

We interviewed and corresponded with many chaplains in order to learn what they considered to be some of the problems that might be barriers to the efficacy of their work. We will discuss here those most frequently mentioned.

With few exceptions, chaplains with whom we communicated stressed the problem of inadequate facilities for worship services. The inability to make arrangements for all patients who wish to attend church services is one of the most common physical drawbacks in the chaplaincy. Few mental hospitals have a chapel. The meeting rooms supplied by the institutions are either too small or inappropriate for an atmosphere of worship. Most are rooms or auditoriums used for other purposes and temporarily adapted for the worship period. Many institutions have such a patient load that even though there may be a chapel, it is not feasible to spare enough attendants to conduct all the patients to it who would like to attend.

Some steps have been taken to fill this need. In one area in which a hospital is located, residents of neighboring communities served by the hospital have raised money to build a chapel on the grounds of the hospital to be used by all religious groups. In Massachusetts space has been made available to the Roman Catholic Archdiocese, the Protestant Council of Churches, and the Rabbinical Association for their own chapels. Roman Catholic chapels have now been built on the grounds of three hospitals, and a fourth is in the planning stage.

The second most frequently mentioned problem is the amount of work to be done within limited hours. In view of all the functions which the chaplains recognize as necessary or possible, it is frustrating to have to accept the feeling of inadequacy caused by sheer lack of time. One of the contributing factors to this situation is the lack of sufficient personnel to meet pastoral needs. (At the present time there is an average of one chaplain to each 1600 patients.) One chaplain reports:

I find that one of the critical problems of my work as chaplain is the need for more chaplains so that we can have the extensive program which will meet the pastoral needs of patients. Mentally ill patients call for much time, and when there is only one full-time chaplain available, he is limited to just so many patients. We could use one full-time chaplain alone to work on our receiving wards to meet the pastoral needs of the newly admitted patients. We could use other chaplain help to work with the patients of our chronic wards and maintain religious services for these patients, who demand a more specialized ministry.

A Roman Catholic chaplain comments: "I can't do anything except administer the sacraments to those people—this limits my time." This chaplain, one of two caring for the spiritual needs of 1200 patients, says that "the only way to begin to do the job is to keep in focus the spiritual needs of the patients and try to eliminate other demands."

Some chaplains pointed to lack of time as the source of other problems: the difficulty of initiating patient relationship and response, and the difficulty of fostering and maintaining helpful relations with other clergy in the community.

Other chaplains, recognizing the critical need for outside pastoral help, list this first among their concerns. One wrote:

We have many community clergymen—some 200 of them—who have come to our hospital for orientations in Religion and Psychology. We could use foundation money to provide more intensive training courses for these men of the local community churches who wish to continue their interest in such a program. In this way we can help with the problems of mental illness on the community level.

The next most frequent concern expressed by our chaplain respondents is lack of adequate salary.

It is illuminating to compare chaplains' salaries with those of some other mental hospital personnel. In Indiana a clinically-trained chaplain is paid the same as a psychologist with a B.A. degree and no previous training. In Wisconsin, a chaplain may receive as much as $1000 less than a psychological trainee. The picture is brighter in Texas, where the chaplain's maximum salary equals that of a chief clinical psychologist—$7800.

The minimum-maximum ranges of chaplains' salaries in the several states are given in Table 1. The average maximum of the

Table 1—Chaplains' Salaries by State

Full Time

Alabama	$3540–4560	Nebraska	$3000 estimated
California	$6060–7356		maximum
Colorado	$4920–6336	New Jersey	$5200–6100
Connecticut	$4200–5640	New York	$6098–7388
Florida	$4140–5280	North Carolina	$4224–5232
Idaho	$3180	North Dakota	$7500 (data
Illinois	$7200 estimated		available for
	maximum; no		State Hospital
	direct reply		only)
Indiana	$4000–5400	Ohio	$4320–6300
Iowa	$4000–6000	Oklahoma	$5000–7000
	estimated		estimated
Kansas	$3360–6360	Oregon	$5040–7860
Kentucky	$3840–4800	Pennsylvania	$5007–7772
Louisiana	$4560–5400	South Carolina	$4914–7150
Maine	$4472–5564	Tennessee	$2400–3480
	estimated	Texas	$4200–7800
Maryland	$5000 estimated	Utah	$2640–3180
	maximum, 1957	Virginia	$5640–7032
Michigan	$4343–6890	Washington	$5184–6168
Minnesota	$6312–7692	Wisconsin	$5640
Missouri	$6280 estimated		estimated
	maximum	District of	
Montana	$5496–6636	Columbia	$7030–8950

Part Time

Massachusetts	$3480* (30-hour week)	Rhode Island	$1000–2250
		Vermont	$1800
New Hampshire	$1200 (half time basis)		estimated

None	No Data Available	
Delaware	Alaska	Mississippi
Wyoming	Arizona	Nevada
	Arkansas	New Mexico
	Georgia	South Dakota
	Hawaii	West Virginia

* Since increased to $5200

SOURCE: National Council of Churches, Department of Pastoral Services, and National Lutheran Council. *Association of Mental Hospital Chaplains Newsletter*, Spring, 1959, Vol. II, No. 1, p. 4. (Adapted.)

thirty-four states (plus District of Columbia) that employ full-time chaplains is $6089 annually, and the average minimum, $4798.

Awareness of the need for adequate compensation for chaplains is not totally lacking on the part of the state governments. A section of the 1957 report of a legislative committee set up in Maryland to study the state's mental hospitals reads in part:

The Committee is gratified with the efforts to afford more ministerial service to the mentally ill in all of the state mental hospitals. However, it believes that the present salary for a full-time religious director of about $5,000 per year is most inadequate and unfair; it therefore recommends that a minimum of $7,500 in this category be established. The value of such service for the mentally ill is immense and is emphasized here.

In 1960 the Commonwealth of Massachusetts increased the salary for chaplains from $3480 to $5200 for a 30-hour week.

Beyond the lack of the essential ingredients—space, time and money—other problems, as seen by the chaplains, are primarily connected with their relationships to hospital staffs and denominations or major faith groups.

The problem of staff relationships is confronted daily and in direct reference to the chaplain's work. One chaplain wrote: "As a hospital chaplain, the most crucial problem which seems to impress itself on my mind is this: How can I achieve a satisfactory relationship with the staff and administration of the hospital so that it will be possible for me to bring a full religious ministry to the patients?" Another writes that many professional staff members seem to cast him continuously in a stereotyped niche. "Probably the most vivid example is the routine way in which patients are referred to me when they are placed on the danger list." This (Protestant) chaplain adds further that "the problem is made more difficult when other chaplains on our staff consciously allow themselves to be 'used' in the stereotyped way without question." In some institutions, chaplains are never directly called upon by the staff except for "extreme unction" or burials, or sometimes for special worship services.

This situation may be a reflection of the fact that, as one chaplain expressed it, "the religious aspect of health (by which I mean wholeness) has long been neglected in our mental hospitals, and even though it is now being accepted, it is only as an 'appendix' to the 'normal' routine of treatment."

Relations between chaplains and their religious groups are a matter of considerable concern. A number of chaplains have indicated a desire not only to receive help from the denominations but also to give help—through information and assistance in mental health programs. "Chaplains are, after all, pastors," one respondent expressed it. "Each one of us belongs to a particular religious group and has sympathies with and a degree of obligation to that group."

Relationships of Protestant chaplains to their religious groups, who sometimes think of the chaplain as "lost to the ministry," have, in many cases, proved unsatisfactory and nonsupportive, sometimes almost nonexistent. Some chaplains have described themselves as being "more or less out of contact" with their denominations. This circumstance of not having a church strongly behind them may also contribute to the sense of isolation, even of inadequacy, frequently expressed by chaplains, and to difficulties in relationships with the hospital staff. The chaplain is "on his own," so to speak, in a way that his associates are not.

Within the network of the chaplain's relationships, that with the patients is the focus of his ministry. Often the relationship between chaplain and patient begins at or soon after the patient's arrival at the hospital. Many chaplains make it a point to see the patient as soon as possible after his admission, both to know something of his religious history and also to allay some of the fearful reaction most patients experience at such a time. Many factors enter into determining whether, after this initial interview, the patient will henceforth maintain an impersonal relationship with the chaplain, or one characterized by warmth, trust, and hope.

Ernest Bruder (1953, b) gives a picture of what the chaplain is likely to be confronted with in such an initial interview:

The patient is often the victim of most unwise and out-dated legal commitment procedures, he is now away from familiar things and people, is behind locked doors, probably feels that he is being punished, and has marked concern as to whether he will ever get out, and, if he does, what will people think of him and will he ever again find employment.

Some of these anxieties can be considerably relieved by a visit from an understanding and properly trained person at the time of admission. This could very well be the chaplain. A patient can find such a visit to be sufficiently reassuring to enable him to speak more freely than he would otherwise, and to take a more positive view of his subsequent treatment.

The focal point of the chaplain's ministry to the patient is the service of worship itself. Louis Linn, M.D., (1955) asks: "If isolation and estrangement from fellow men are the common lot of psychotic patients, what could possibly be more logical than to bring these lonely people together in an emotionally meaningful situation? And what more natural group can we provide for them than that of the religious congregation?"

More patients participate in religious services than in any other voluntary "extra-curricular" activity in our mental hospitals. Father William Sullivan, Roman Catholic chaplain at Metropolitan State Hospital at Waltham, Massachusetts, points out that even some patients who won't go to meals will go to mass. When a seriously sick person is able to interfere with his preoccupations, his own non-action, and go to a religious service, this can be important for health and may be indicative of more faith than the average well person has.

In pastoral relations with individual patients a chaplain will ordinarily attend first to those patients who have shown loneliness, fear, feelings of guilt, and who have made explicit or implicit references to religion (including hostile expressions, which sometimes may be interpreted as more hopeful than indifference). Patients are sometimes selected for individual pastoral work with the chaplain on the basis of expressed religious concern, often expressed in seemingly nonreligious ways.

The chaplain's perception of the patient is a crucial factor in the relationship. Chaplain Keith W. Keidel (1957) sees the patient as one whose meaningful relationships have been interrupted and distorted and whose relationships with others, with the objective world, and with himself now lack meaning, support, and flexibility. His body and his feelings, in addition to his relationships, are impaired. The patient's fear intensifies pain. But pain is not necessarily destructive; it can be a force toward integration. The chaplain tries to understand the ways in which the patient is reaching out—or fears to reach out—to communicate his feelings, which, while they may be distorted, are nonetheless real. "When I look at the patient," says Chaplain Keidel, "I am looking at myself. If I accept the patient, I am accepting part of myself. This is the reverence for personality created by God in an image I do not yet totally understand, totally feel, or totally perceive."

Thomas W. Klink (1958), Chaplain at Topeka State Hospital, feels that the pastor's acquired ability to listen, and to reflect and elicit feelings, is not much help with acutely disturbed patients. Rather, the chaplain must offer his own sense of identity, limits, and differentiated ideas to patients who have experienced "decompensation" from adult ways of behaving to primitive, infantile levels.

Chaplain Klink emphasizes the importance of movement and function in communication with regressed patients. "Communication must adopt the syntax of action if it is to be heard." The necessity for metaphoric communication with the deeply disturbed is met in part by the chaplain's training and fluency in the language of metaphor—though the metaphors used should not be limited to religious symbolism.

Continuing relationships with the family are important not only to the individual patients, but also to all those concerned with their care; family acceptance and genuine concern for the ill member may contribute to his recovery. Often, however, the family is a part of the negative or destructive background of the patient; further, the entrance of the patient into the hospital puts the family on the defensive. They are embarrassed, hostile, reticent or a combination of these. A recent study disclosed that some families have an unconscious tendency to push the ill member further into his illness—and once he is sent to a hospital, want him to stay there. The chaplain can be instrumental in helping the family understand and accept the patient and his illness. But the chaplain cannot work alone to this end; he needs the cooperation of the patient's pastor and of other clergymen in the community.

The greater the understanding and acceptance of the realistic picture of mental illness, by the patient's family and by the community at large, the better can those who are dealing with the individual patient, during and after his hospitalization, help him to find a normal social life.

Dr. Harry Solomon (1959), Massachusetts Commissioner of Mental Health, points to specific needs in community mental health education that can be supported by the chaplain and the parish clergyman:

Although many patients in state mental hospitals have been committed voluntarily, most have come in under a court decree. Though today, more and more are coming to mental hospitals on a voluntary basis, we have not reached the point where the mental hospital is an institution which a patient enters and leaves freely and voluntarily, as he does, for example, a general hospital. There has been much progress in the direction of liberalizing the basis of discharge. However, one great barrier which still stands in the way is the objection on the part of the community at large to mental patients having any freedom. Thus, both the chaplain and the clergyman in the parish can contribute greatly to facilitating this movement by becoming familiar with the legal machinery regarding commitment through the courts, and through educational efforts to change attitudes towards the patient and towards mental illness in general.

A goal of some mental health workers and others concerned with community education regarding mental illness is to foster community responsibility. Alfred P. Bay, M.D., (1956) writes:

If the mental hospital is to be redefined as an integrated part of a long treatment-and-rehabilitation continuum, having its focus in the patient's own community, with hospitalization regarded as only an episode in this continuum, then present mental health education will have to be sharply revised to emphasize acceptance of the mentally ill person as a community responsibility rather than a state responsibility.

If this trend is followed, the chaplain's role takes on further dimensions.

Three closely related contemporary trends in mental patient care that may have further implications for the chaplain are, (1) attempts to avoid isolating the patient from his family and community, (2) the increasing emphasis on rehabilitation rather than sheer custody, and (3) special rehabilitation programs with chronic patients. These trends are described by Dr. Walter E. Barton (1959), Superintendent of the Boston State Hospital, as follows:

1. A primary means of avoiding the prolonged separation of the patient from his home and community is to move the patient back into the community as swiftly as possible in order to reduce the length of time he is separated from his family and his job. The movement in this direction is indicated by statistics from the Boston State Hospital. In 1949, 55 per cent of all patients under the age of sixty were released within 125 days. A decade later, 75 per cent of patients under sixty are released within ninety days. Yet this is not soon enough, for the trauma of change and separation still occurs, and the avoidance of hospitalization itself is sought as an ideal. By keeping the individual who is suffering from a mental disorder on an out-patient basis and, where necessary, extending psychiatric services into the community and into the home, those responsible for helping him can avert the trauma of separation and isolation that occurs with hospitalization, and at the same time make use of and, where possible, improve whatever supportive factors can be found in his environment.

Other variations of this approach are the day hospital, which makes it possible for the patient to be with his family at night, and the night hospital, which enables him to continue with his job while using the hospital as a "home base."

2. The movement from custody to rehabilitation. The image of the ideal patient held by staff members of most mental hospitals in this country is the quiet, well-behaved patient who gives the staff no trouble. One consequence of this conception is the practice of static, custodial control which is intended to reduce the possibility of the patient's resistance to established institutions and routines, and by virtue of which the individuality and identity of the patient are reduced to a minimum.

The change that we are seeking to bring about and that we have succeeded in bringing about in a few hospitals, is a departure from the custodial, static philosophy of patient care and an approach to a more dynamic program of rehabilitation. This involves giving much greater responsibility to the patients for the management of their own needs and relationships and fuller opportunity for self-expression. It implies, on the part of the administration and staff, greater awareness of the social setting and the removal of many of the barriers to social interaction between patient and staff and between patient and patient. It means having greater respect for the individual patient. Such a change will bring an inevitable by-product which we must be ready to accept and deal with and of which the chaplain must be aware—namely, an increase in anxiety on the part of the staff.

3. The third trend is rehabilitation as a specialized activity with a limited number of chronic patients. The hospital's environment itself can be made conducive to treatment and not only to custody. A paradox may be seen in the fact that more and more personnel may be brought into the out-patient and community phases of treatment, as well as into programs of prevention, and thus make fewer available for this specialized program with chronic patients. Yet many steps can be taken by other than medical personnel. Such a program would be a concentrated effort based on the philosophy of social interaction and on the fact that chemotherapy makes it possible to relieve symptoms sufficiently to work effectively with patients who might otherwise be unreachable.

Research and experimental programs indicate the need to develop the potential of the patient until he can be self-sufficient. The danger of releasing a patient before satisfactory autonomy and ego strength have been attained is illustrated by the experience of some patients who are released from the hospital and return to their families. If the patient fails to come up to the expectations of his wife, she may well push him back into his illness. The patient who returns to his parental home often gets protection and support from his parents. They are glad to have a "child" again and play the roles he needs to protect and reinforce his regression; the old level of relationships prolongs and intensifies his chronicity. If these relationships are later disturbed or the support removed, the patient may relapse.

Even a partial transition from custody to treatment, such as would be represented by a rehabilitation program with a limited number of patients, is an involved process requiring careful orientation for both patients and staff. The mental hospital patient tends to take on the goals and values of the group he identifies with, as does a member of any group. If the patient is to be rehabilitated, he must be motivated to change his goals and status, to be willing to face the anxiety that the loss of support may bring. Other patients and staff must be willing to support the patient in the changes through which he progresses. While the patient needs experience in handling increasing responsibility, independence, and self-expression, as ties are gradually loosened, he must also be helped to progress towards acceptable norms. This implies not only changes of social attitudes and behavior but also the development of skills in performance of work.

At all these levels, the chaplain is not the person responsible for the action, but he is supportive to it. He must be aware of the steps the patient is going through. He can influence the interchange between patient and patient, and between patient and staff. The chaplain has—and can communicate—faith that an individual can change and that he can advance, and that he won't be abandoned in the course of that advance.

We have not attempted a comprehensive study of the mental hospital chaplaincy. Rather, in partial answer to the question, "What are the churches doing in the area of mental health?" we have discussed certain critical aspects of one ministry. Many more questions remain to be asked in regard to the chaplaincy, such as the following:

Is the chaplain's role primarily one of *being* or one of *doing?* To what extent, for instance, does the chaplain as a "representative of God" become an identification object in the lives of patients, and as such, serve as a therapeutic agent in the healing process? If he serves only in this capacity, is his presence in the hospital justified? Should religious groups settle for meeting the worship needs of their hospitalized parishioners, and only later survey and re-evaluate the chaplaincy role? Can the chaplain then ultimately become a friend, a father, a channel to reality, an inspiration to personal hope and effort? Must the mentally ill person be healed before he can be open to religious conceptions? Anton Boisen believes that mental illness in some cases can be the opening up to the possibilities of religious orientation. Is the chaplain to stand by and await the healing, or participate in it, or try to find limited areas where contact may be made? What is the chaplain's vision of the "healed patient"? Does he see him only in two alternative identities: patient or parishioner? What is the chaplain's attitude towards suffering: Does he think it should have a particular result, or that it should merely cease? Is the chaplain's frame of reference beneficial to a patient in some way that a psychiatrist's could not be beneficial? In short, do patients need something in addition to psychiatry, or different from psychiatry? If so, are clergymen able to recognize what this need is, and are they able to fill it? We do not have the answers to these questions. But finding answers to such questions as these—or perhaps the persistent asking of such questions—may contribute to a continuing definition and assessment of the chaplain's work.

CONCLUSIONS

1. The chaplain's position in the mental hospital community differs in many ways from that of the pastor in the parish. Two of these differences contribute significantly to the uniqueness, and, to some extent, to the isolation of his position. The first concerns the chaplain's potential parishioners, the patients, who are not in the hospital because they are religious, nor because they belong to the chaplain's religious group, nor because they are Catholic or Protestant or Jewish, but because they are ill. Perhaps more important, they are under varying degrees of restraint. They are spending their lives—for the time being at least—in a psychological realm whose limits are wanting to get better or not wanting to get better, wanting

to get out of the hospital or wanting to live out their lives there, believing that they are sick or believing they are not. Their relation to the chaplain must be seen in the secondary place it occupies in their total present experience.

A second difference concerns the chaplain's potential peers, the other staff members of the hospital. The professional personnel in the hospital are there presumably because of their ability to deal effectively with illness. The chaplain is in the hospital not essentially because he is a good therapist but because of his religious office. It is true that the chaplain usually has to have certain special qualifications beyond his religious training. Further, the church has traditionally not neglected the mentally ill, and its concern that the patient should have spiritual help explains the presence of the chaplain. Yet the chaplain is not in any real sense the spiritual leader of a congregation, unlike the minister in the local parish, who is the head of the religious community. In the hospital community it is the psychiatric staff who have the power of decision; the chaplain is fairly far down the line in this nonclerical hierarchy, an important but auxiliary member. This division of concern—religion for the chaplain, illness for all the others—has important consequences for the way in which the chaplain is seen by both patients and staff, and for the way in which he comes to view himself.

2. In interviews with nurses, attendants, clinical directors, and superintendents of mental hospitals we found, with some exceptions, a warm appreciation of the chaplain and his work. Yet both chaplains and medical staff expressed strong desires for better communication and relationships. Although the hospital—or, more exactly, the state—pays the salary of the chaplain, his presence is initiated from "outside," by the churches. Partly because of this, some administrators and staff members feel that the prospect for better relationships and better intercommunications depends mainly on the chaplain, whom they expect to initiate the greater interchange by defining his own role.

Dr. Harry Solomon (1959) points out that chaplaincy work in the past consisted largely of the conducting of worship services, usually by visiting clergymen who had little other contact with the hospital.

The chaplaincy, as we know it today, was not instituted by the government nor by the mental hospitals, but rather by the churches themselves. The chaplaincy is a very valuable part of the total treatment program. However, it may be this fact that it was brought in from outside, rather than initiated from within, that it was a freely offered gift, that we really understand so little about what the chaplain really is.

The administration, the superintendents, the staff, all recognize as clearly as the chaplains do themselves that greater communication between staff and chaplains is badly needed. However, this increase in communication should be initiated by the chaplain. A great contribution in this direction would be a clear delineation of his work. Many chaplains have expressed the feeling that they would like the superintendent to define the chaplain's role. This definition should be a self-engendered thing; in other words, the definition, the delineation can best be done by the chaplains themselves.

Father William Sullivan (1959), Roman Catholic chaplain at Metropolitan State Hospital, Waltham, Massachusetts, and former president of the Association of Mental Hospital Chaplains, points out that the first concern of the chaplain is the needs of the patients in the realm of the spiritual, territory largely unknown to the superintendent and to the staff. The chaplain also works in a therapeutc way, though informally and indirectly, by being concerned with some of the by-products of mental illness. For example, the hopelessness and infantilism of the schizophrenic is a primary concern of the chaplain and one area in which he can be of great aid. Father Sullivan raises the question whether part of the problem regarding communication may be simply that the chaplains do not verbalize sufficiently.

Though their work is flexible and very often undefined, and though the chaplain himself must be ready to seize creatively upon new needs and find opportunities for his help in many areas, his role, his already structured life situation in which he finds himself, his auxiliary aid to the therapeutic team are already defined and already have found focus and direction. All he needs to do now is to spell it out.

3. A clergyman who has the responsibility for pastoral relationships with 1,000 or more "parishioner-patients" is not likely to see

any one of them often on a personal basis. A partial solution, at least, would be to increase the number of chaplains. The number of professional patient-care personnel in all public mental hospitals averages 2.8 per 100 patients. The recommended average for registered nurses is one nurse for each five patients, and for psychologists, one for each 100 patients. The present average for chaplains is one per 1,600 patients (this ratio varies greatly from hospital to hospital and from state to state; the ratio is based on the census of mental hospital patients—i.e., 640,000 average on any one day). Almost all the 400 mental hospital chaplains are paid by the states, the approximately two million dollars in salaries far exceeding the total amount spent by the churches of this country for their mental health endeavors, including their support of the 21 church-supported mental hospitals.

Although there are many economic problems and problems involving church-state relations that must be considered, the churches might take under advisement the possibility of supporting an equal number of chaplains as do the states. The new ratio which would thus be made possible—one chaplain to each 800 patients—would begin to approximate the ratio of clergymen to church members in the community at large.

4. The effectiveness of a chaplain is facilitated not only by his own mobility and availability—a chaplain who gets around the hospital frequently can do more for the patients in general than one who is tied up with problems or administrative duties—but also by the attitudes of the staff and of the denomination or council of churches he represents. These attitudes affect not only his motivation and other inner dispositions, but also his freedom, and other procedural matters. But in the long run, the effectiveness of the chaplain seems to depend on his being an adult human being, a healthy personality himself.

5. Many of our state and county mental hospitals are predominantly custodial institutions in which the chaplains are limited to fulfilling traditional roles as stabilizing agents. Some chaplains with whom we have communicated express dissatisfaction and frustration at finding themselves stereotyped in such passive roles,

and a sometimes bitter awareness of the difficulty of maintaining significant relationships with patients in institutions whose philosophy is primarily custody rather than rehabilitation. Many chaplains feel that only a greater understanding of the social and cultural dynamics of the mental hospital community and more familiarity with abnormal psychology, group processes, and principles of milieu therapy will increase their effectiveness. And some have expressed the strong feeling that their greatest contribution to the welfare of the patients—apart from conducting religious services and giving personal pastoral care to a limited number of patients—may lie in the areas of total milieu therapy and group dynamics.

6. Many chaplains feel the need for more clinical experience, preferably under the supervision of psychiatrists in addition to chaplain-supervisors, and for a longer period of time—one or two full years, for example, rather than two summers. Some have suggested the desirability of personal analysis, though this is not often feasible. Through the longer and deeper experience the chaplain will not only become more thoroughly acquainted with the manifestations of mental illness, but, more particularly, will gain a greater understanding of the "inner world" of the mental patient and of his own "inner world."

The goal of such a recommendation is not to make the chaplain a better "therapist" in the technical sense, but a better "communicator" as a chaplain. It is suggested by way of an approach rather than content. It may enable him to get on the "wave-length" of the patients, to understand them better at their symbolic level. For example, if the chaplain sees the Gospel as the most significant content of his communication with patients, he will then know in what terms it can be made most meaningful to the patients and will be better able to communicate with them in those terms.

III

Changing Roles of the Parish Clergy

In the preceding chapter we focused upon the most direct role of church and clergy in mental health matters—namely, the mental hospital chaplaincy and its functions and problems and contributions.

In this chapter and in the following four, we consider some of the more indirect ways in which the church has relevance for mental health as the clergy explore ways to deal with the "normal" rather than the pathological, with the troubled rather than the sick, and to work on a level of prevention in the congregation and in the community, rather than as members of the "healing team" in the mental hospital.

First, we examine some changes in the role and image of the clergy.

THE PROTESTANT MINISTER

In *The Purpose of the Church and Its Ministry,* H. Richard Niebuhr (1956, p. 50) of Yale Divinity School refers to the ministry today as "the perplexed profession":

Neither ministers nor the schools that nurture them are guided today by a clear-cut, generally accepted conception of the office of the ministry. . . . The evidence that perplexity and vagueness continue to affect thought about the ministry is to be found today in the theological schools and among ministers themselves. Some schools and some pastors are highly conscious of the problem; others are in a more difficult state because they have not yet realized the source of their perplexities.

A step toward clarification of the situation of "the perplexed profession" is a recent study of ministerial roles among 690 Protestant clergymen. The author, Samuel Blizzard, examined what ministers do with their time, what they would like to do with their time, and what parishioners expect them to do with their time. "The new American culture has effected a change of what people expect of the minister," writes Dr. Blizzard (1956). "In the past, the parish clergyman has performed his functions as a general practitioner. Now increasingly he is expected to be a specialist." A specialist with a single aim and function might have a more readily definable role. The Protestant minister tries to fulfill the demands made on him, and in meeting them has to fill several roles, in each of which he is expected to be a specialist. Conflict and stress appear not so much in the performance of these roles as in the increasing demands for specialization in all of them.

In a one-clergyman parish the minister appears to be a kind of "general manager," but is actually required, by subtle demands, to be his own committee of specialists. Shortcomings in any of the six central roles—administrator, organizer, pastor, preacher, priest, teacher—can undermine his over-all effectiveness.

As administrator, the minister must often supervise the financial program of the church and coordinate the work of its staff. As organizer, he must participate in intra- and inter-denominational activities and be active in community affairs. As pastor he serves his congregants in a person-to-person relationship. As priest, he administers sacraments, conducts marriages, funerals and other rites of passage, and leads in services of worship. As preacher, he tries to provide guidance and inspiration in a one-to-many relationship with his parishioners. As teacher, he directs the church's religious education program and "teaches" in many other less defined ways.

Not only is every minister expected to be a specialist in each of these simultaneously, but he must adapt his personal preferences among these roles to the requirements and interests—and sometimes the whims—of the congregants.

In terms of the relative amount of time spent on these subfunctions of the ministry—which reflects to some extent parishioners' expectations of the clergy—Blizzard found the following ranking:

Administrator	two-fifths
Pastor	one-fourth
Preacher-priest	one-fifth
Organizer	one-tenth
Teacher	one-twentieth

After being queried as to how they apportioned their time, these clergymen were also asked what they felt was most important, what they were most effective in, and what they most enjoyed. Then the responses were quite different. The roles of administrator and organizer were ranked lowest, preacher and pastor were ranked highest on all three counts.

Lack of congruence between the pastor's personal preference and the parishioners' expectations does not inevitably imply insupportable conflict. Yet it may well be a source of considerable psychological stress. That the conflict is ever intense enough to cause the minister to break down is, however, open to question. Competition, conflict, and confusion among roles may be a product of the pastor's own personality difficulties, rather than a cause of them, though it is equally precarious to point to the direction of causation as to claim a causal relationship.

Some clergymen seem to have less sense of role conflict than others. A pastor who is free of such conflict may have great gifts of flexibility, or may have defined his role as a "servant," whose service consists simply in helping man live closer to God.

Both Blizzard (1956) and Nameche (1958) found that clergymen spend more time in administrative tasks than in any other, and report their administrative chores to be the most frustrating of all. Most ministers neither enjoy these duties, nor consider themselves effective in them, nor consider these tasks particularly relevant to the goals of their ministry.

The role of the clergyman as an *organizer* of intra- and inter-denominational and community activities seems to assume greater and greater proportions, yet clergymen generally do not consider this work important or enjoyable. Even less do they consider themselves effective in it. But the feeling on the part of congregations about their pastor's involvement in organizational work is almost always one of approval.

In the role of *pastor*—shepherd of the flock—clergymen report that they find the greatest fulfillment of their professional life. (Here we are including the total pastoral function of dealing with people on a personal basis; this includes but is not limited to pastoral counseling.) Many pastors have expressed sentiments similar to this remark by one informant: "The interpersonal relations of pastoral care have definitely sustained me when the rest of my ministry appeared fruitless and meaningless."

Interviews conducted during the course of our community studies show varied reactions by parishioners to one aspect of the pastoral function: the pastoral call. They range from expressions of some uneasiness, and a disparagement of "small-talk," to serious communication and interpersonal concern. There is no doubt considerable symbolic value in the pastoral call. Here, especially in cases of sickness, the concern of the church and of the community, as well as of the pastor, is communicated to the parishioner and appears to have helpful effects. This matter will be treated again later when we discuss intervention in crisis and pre-crisis situations.

In terms of the church community at large, the pastoral role of the clergyman would theoretically be of great importance. With the increasing role-differentiation of the clergyman's work, it seems possible that the minister could be, for example, a good preacher, and at the same time less competent in interpersonal relationships. If this is the case, the local church may be held together by something other than the pastor's concern for, and pastoral relationships with, his individual congregants. The church becomes less of a community and more of an organization, guided by structured sanctions and rules. The more spontaneous religious community may be a kind of milieu in which individual lives are "transformed"; the more normative religious organization, in which the clergyman as *pastor* is less effective and determinative, may be one in which lives are stabilized. Which is more significant for mental health is a matter of conjecture.

For most clergymen the role of preacher is primary in their

evaluation of their work, although it is given only one-fifth of their time. Preaching is thus another area of potential role conflict. There is some evidence that "tranquilizer," or peace-of-mind, sermons are the best received by many congregations. Accompanying this rise of the peace-of-mind sermon is an observable decline of the prophetic type. It is hazardous to try to evaluate such trends in terms of mental health. Perhaps we could make a somewhat oversimplified comparison: Preaching that promises some sort of *removal* of one's problems may be unhealthy, both psychologically and theologically. Preaching that purports to help people live with their problems, transcend them, and see them for what they really are, is both psychologically and theologically healthy.

Clear discernment of the varying and often conflicting roles of the clergyman can be a contribution not only to greater understanding of the actual or potential stress but also to a reduction, if not resolution, of the conflict. In an empirical study based on interviews with Protestant, Jewish, and Roman Catholic clergymen in two cities, Luke M. Smith (1958) points to the three important roles of the clergyman:

1. As congregational leader, in which the clergyman forms a small and permanent fellowship group "which mediates between the individual and the mass society."

2. As symbolizer (combining preacher, teacher, and ritualist) in which the clergyman creates a reference group and serves as a translator and transmitter of ideas to (and from) them.

3. As pastoral counselor, a role whose increasing emphasis may be an adaptation to the needs of a more individualized and mobile society, and in which the clergyman deals with individual and unique needs.

Dr. Smith emphasizes the latent functions of the clergyman's roles and points out that within the multiplicity of roles, the clergyman may think of one as his central role. Emphasis on counseling was found to decrease strains between various roles, "thereby indicating that counseling is an adaptation to a more extensive and individualized social structure whose needs cannot be met so well by the greater rigidity implied in symbolizing and congregational fellowship."

We may discern three additional roles that to some extent overlap and interpenetrate those we have described: namely, those of prophet, "cultural mediator," and counselor.

The role of prophet seems to fall sometimes within the preaching role, with some carry-over to teaching. The clergyman as prophet has been studied recently by E. Campbell and T. Pettigrew (1959) with reference to a group of ministers in Little Rock, Arkansas. The authors describe the assumption of the prophetic task by a few clergymen—the task of criticizing the contemporary social situation —as being undertaken at the peril of their careers. The authors also show how the role of prophet is sometimes avoided even by clergymen with strong convictions about an issue, who temper these convictions for the sake of security and prestige.

The prophet—critic of social inertia or initiator of social change— is an anomaly when religion is a part of the popular and respectable way of life. The role sometimes signifies a break with the established order, and is, therefore, nonadjustive by definition. Sometimes the prophetic function of criticism and protest is an antidote to complacency and can give vitality and high purpose to the ministry and to the life of the congregation. But sometimes the disparity between the actual and the ideal is too great. At some point in the process of the church's long-range accommodation to the social order a "prophetic break" may occur. This has often been the origin of sect-type religious groups—pentecostal, holiness, and adventist. Members of these groups—the nation's "fourth religion"—are critics not only of the social order but of the established churches which seem to have capitulated to it.

The role of "cultural mediator" cuts across the preaching, teaching, and organizing functions. In this, the clergyman is a mediator between the religious institution and society at large. As a cultural mediator the clergyman can become a source of political, intellectual, or social involvement for his congregation, and a channel to such involvement. He can interpret developments in such fields as psychiatry and relate them to the needs and interests of his parishioners. The role of cultural mediator is always latent in the profession of the clergy, and when actualized, can be highly effective at critical focal points of social change.

The role of counselor falls within the pastoral role, being one of several pastoral functions the minister carries on. (Blizzard made no distinction, in the research to which we have referred, among counseling, calling, and other pastoral duties, but used the pastoral role to include them all.) The minister as counselor is perhaps the one role in which the relations between religion and mental health are most sharply illuminated. The counseling portion of a minister's pastoral duties on the average takes only a small segment of his time; yet it is considered to be a crucial aspect of pastoral life. The minister-as-counselor will be our primary concern in subsequent chapters; and our discussion here of the wider role-complex of the clergy may help to place counseling in its proper perspective.

THE ROMAN CATHOLIC PRIEST

The Roman Catholic Church is the largest religious body in the United States, and its clergy are the largest group of ordained persons. Although some aspects of our discussion of the roles of Protestant clergy are applicable to clergy of other faiths, we shall consider some sociological aspects of the Catholic priesthood, and some of the differences that emerge in comparison with the Protestant clergy.

A primary contrast between the Roman Catholic and the Protestant clergy is the distinction between laity and clergy. In the Roman church the clergy occupy a status and perform functions that in no way can be confused with the role of the layman (although much greater participation by laymen in various aspects of the church's life and work has been fostered by such movements as the Lay Apostolate). In most Protestant churches, what has been called the "democratization of religion" (following largely from the concept of the priesthood of all believers) is always latent and often manifest.

A second difference between priest and minister occurs in the extensiveness of their respective "secular" involvements. The priest is often viewed, whether rightly or wrongly, as being outside the patterns of secular life. The boundaries of the priest's authority and competence are prescribed by Canon Law to lie within the area of "faith and morals." Although this area is difficult to delimit and define, it is in general more clearly circumscribed by Catholicism than by Protestantism.

Dr. John D. Donovan (1951) of Boston College has described an important historical shift along these lines—one that applies, in varying degrees, to clergy of all faiths, but more particularly to the Catholic priest. In the "old country" the priest was often the only educated man in the community. Because of his learning he was an authority not only in his special domain of faith and morals but also on secular matters—finance, employment, education, politics, and the like. His personal advice on such topics and his public pronouncements on them were received as authoritative, and honored by the community. As other sources of advice and guidance increased, the priest was relegated more and more frequently to his own area of specialization, "faith and morals."

A third distinction between minister and priest as described by Dr. Donovan concerns relationship to the flock. By canonical definition, the priest's relation to his parishioner is described as "affectively neutral."

Thus, the priest is expected, in relations with the laity, to be "affectively neutral" and to act in an impersonal, dispassionate manner regardless of the gravity or emotional intensity attached to the special problems of his parishioner. As a functionary of the Church his role can recognize the problems of his parishioners only as ones for which provisions are made in the doctrine and laws of the organization.

Such specifications as these reflect the wisdom of the Church in structuring the total role of the priest in such a way as to provide for the dual requirement of the priest, and for equilibrium between alternating emphases from the liturgical to the more personal, particularistic functions.

A further difference to be noted between the priest and the minister is symbolized in the appellation, "Father" (though members of the Episcopal church sometimes use the term for their clergy). In a study of the social role of the priest, Father Jean Marie Jammes (1955) of Lyons, France, analyzed responses from 389 Catholic laymen in an American city. Discussing this form of address, he writes: "For the layman the priest is not a specialist in a sociological sense. (The priest is primarily, 'Father.') His relationship to his people is based on the familial concept more than on the idea of specialization." Father Jammes, like Dr. Donovan, claims that the priest is a director and guide by virtue of his ascribed authority, not his personal achievements. (In regard to counseling, responses from some of our interviews indicate that people tend to go to a certain priest for help because of his human qualities, his accessibility and the like, and not because of ecclesiastical, charismatic, or ascribed attributes.)

THE RABBI

In a sociological study of the American Rabbi, Jerome E. Carlin and Saul H. Mendlovitz (1958, p. 378) of the University of Chicago, assert that the Rabbi can best be understood as a religious specialist who is attempting "to cope with changes in the Jewish community which seriously undermined traditional authority structures."

The early rabbi . . . based his authority on an intimate knowledge of the written and oral law, both of which he claimed were divinely revealed. He was responsible for the elaboration of this body of sacred literature and was the creator and product of those institutions which bound the Jews together in the Diaspora—the school and the synagogue.

These activities led to an important development of rabbinic occupational roles in which the teacher, the judge, the spiritual leader of the synagogue, and the official community leader become clearly delineated.

All of these role developments were, however, subordinate to an even more significant rabbinic role, that of "scholar-saint."

The "scholar-saint" ideal of the rabbi has dominated Jewish history from the beginning of the rabbinic office. The primary obligation of the scholar-saint was (and is) to know and teach the Law and live according to its precepts; his claim to leadership rested entirely on learning and personal piety.

Traditional religious institutions and authorities in Judaism have become progressively weakened since the Middle Ages by the impact of many forces, including those of the humanistic Enlightenment, and the Industrial Revolution. This low ebb of Jewish religious history has been called by Salo Baron (1932), "the Jewish Emancipation." This breakdown of some of the foundations of the Jewish community is still in progress the world over, and requires increasing adjustment by Jewish religious specialists. In this light, we can look more closely into the roles of American rabbis.

Selecting a stratified random sample of the rabbinate in a large American city, Carlin and Mendlovitz conducted personal interviews with rabbis representing Orthodox, Reform and Conservative groups. The authors distinguished seven types of rabbis. These include three types of Orthodox Rabbi (the Traditional, the Free-Lance, and the Modern); three types of Reform Rabbi (the Intellectual, the Social, and the Traditionalistic); and the Conservative Rabbi.

Although in each of these types of rabbi the "scholar-saint" ideal still prevails, it does so to differing degrees. The more modern, less traditionalistic rabbis tend to subordinate the scholar-saint role to the more functional roles seen in the Protestant clergy. Thus, being a preacher, teacher, pastor, priest, organizer, or administrator sometimes submerges the historical Jewish ideal of "knowing and living the Law."

Perhaps more strongly than is the case with other minority groups, the Jews in this country constantly experience two opposing pulls. One is to regain and retain the autonomy of their community and tradition; the other is toward assimilation, sometimes accompanied by compromises necessary for individual survival and advancement. Both the effectiveness of the rabbi and the evaluation of his work in terms of mental health may rest on the extent to which he can balance these two tendencies.

The Traditional Orthodox rabbi, in the typology derived by Carlin and Mendlovitz, seeks to restore the totality of Jewish life before the Emancipation. He attempts to embody the role of the original scholar-saint in all of its Orthodox fullness. Carlin and Mendlovitz point out that Orthodox rabbis have increasingly less influence on the American Jewish community. Most have come from some part of Eastern Europe, and strongly resist any degree of assimilation into the American culture. Because of such tendencies in ultra-orthodox groups, the Traditional rabbis may be a contributing cause of some stress in all but members of the older generation.

The "Free-Lance" Orthodox rabbi rarely has a formal affiliation with any synagogue or school. His function consists primarily in performing religious rites—weddings, funerals, Bar Mitzvahs, and the like—for individual families who are not members of a synagogue, or conducting special services such as Rosh Hashonah and Yom Kippur for a congregation without a rabbi.

The Modern Orthodox rabbi is characterized by orthodox theology and a modern approach. He takes seriously the task of returning the Jews to their traditional faith, but he uses up-to-date methods of doing it. His synagogue often takes on the appearance of a community center, and the emphasis of his rabbinate becomes mainly educational and administrative. The Modern Orthodox rabbi seems to have maintained balance between cultural autonomy and cultural assimilation.

With all of the Reform rabbis we clearly see a specialization of roles. The Intellectual Reform rabbi takes on all six of the major role functions of the Protestant clergy, but specializes in preaching and teaching, thus deviating most from the scholar-saint ideal of tradition. Although he is a scholar, his scholarship is usually in matters other than the Law. His work tends much more toward assimilation into the larger cultural body and away from the preservation of Jewish autonomy. The Intellectual Reform rabbi, the most characteristic of Reform rabbis, responds to the loss of authority of the rabbinic office by replacing the scholar-saint ideal with the secular-scholar ideal.

The Social Reform rabbi is a variation on and, to some extent, a reaction against the Intellectual Reform model. The Social Reformer is equally liberal about discarding traditional aspects of Judaism, but he emphasizes social rather than intellectual compensations for the old order. Carlin and Mendlovitz point out that, "The Social

Reformer is oriented toward the realization and fulfillment of democratic values in contemporary society." Thus, he functions with greater vigor as an administrator and organizer. In general, he too influences his congregants away from the minority community status and toward assimilation by the American culture.

The Traditionalistic Reform rabbi works toward the "reassertion of Jewish culture," but would not have it take on Orthodox forms (such as strict adherence to dietary laws). He seeks to restore historic Judaism and sees himself as a priest of the old order. He emphasizes both the traditionalistic-communal and the modern-assimilative requirements in Jewish life, and thus tends to promote sociological and psychological stability for his parishioners.

The Conservative rabbi represents a position midway between the Orthodox and Reform groups; that is, he represents tradition but is not afraid of innovations. "He has been characterized as a religious specialist who faced the problem of the breakdown of traditional authority with a middle-of-the-road program." The Conservative rabbi also signifies a reassertion of the scholar-saint ideal, perhaps in its most serious modern manifestation. Because of the conflict between this ideal and the demands that he become an effective "promoter" (administrator and organizer), the Conservative rabbi seems, more than others, to suffer from the role conflict discernible among the Protestant clergy. If, in this dilemma, the Conservative rabbi can retain the tenuous balance between his Orthodox and Modern dispositions, it is likely, Carlin and Mendlovitz believe, that he may find the most successful solution to the spiritual-psychological estrangements of the contemporary American Jew. "Although he is still far from the scholar-saint role, as an organizer he has not only been able 'to stem the tide of indifference' resulting from the Emancipation, but has had remarkable success in gaining adherents to his movement."

Carlin and Mendlovitz summarize the situation of the rabbinate (p. 413-414):

There are, then, three elements which appear to contain the most characteristic features of the Modern Orthodox, Conservative, and Traditional Reform roles and which attest to the proposition that a common rabbinic role is emerging, namely: (1) all three types of rabbis have been characterized as organizers in so far as they are presently engaged in organizing and rebuilding the Jewish community about the synagogue; (2) all to a large extent perform a similar complex of functions, including preaching (in English), teaching, pastoral visitation and counselling, priestly functions, administrative functions, and engaging in numerous activities in the Jewish and non-Jewish community; (3) all aspire to a scholar-saint role.

Thus it appears that the scholar-saint role which from the time of the early rabbi was the most characteristic rabbinic role in the Jewish community, but which was submerged under the impact of Emancipation, is once again destined to re-emerge as the most characteristic rabbinic role. The new scholar-saint will, undoubtedly, differ from the traditional type. It seems likely that some of the functions which the contemporary rabbi has assumed—preaching, priestly functions, pastoral work, and some communal activity—will find a place in the new role. . . . Whatever may be the uncertainty and indefiniteness of the new rabbinic scholar-saint role, authority will be based on knowing and living the Law, and to the extent that a community will be built up around the Law the rabbi will be its religious specialist.

Role conflict and change can be dynamic and creative in themselves. They can stimulate the clergyman to formulate more flexible and comprehensive—or, as the case may be, more limited—definitions of his role, to clarify his parishioners' perception of him, and his own image of himself, thereby making some of the latent potentialities in his profession more manifest. If, however, the predominant effect of issues of role and identity on the individual clergyman is frustration, tension, or other stress, his potentiality as a mental health resource may be greatly reduced. More hazardously, he may identify his own inner conflicts with those he perceives in his professional life. Then "what the church is doing in mental health work" may become what the individual clergyman is doing for his own salvation and not for the sake of his parishioners.

Though there are highly relevant possibilities for mental health in several roles of the parish clergyman, in the following three chapters we will pay particular attention to the clergy's activities which seem to be most closely associated with mental health: namely, pastoral counseling.

IV

Trends in Pastoral Counseling

JUDAISM

ALTHOUGH THE roles of priest and prophet, as well as that of scholar-saint, dominated the Biblical period of Judaism, references are also found in this period to the religious counselor to whom the lay Jew would come in private to talk about his personal problems. Rabbi Henry Enoch Kagan (1959), founder of the Committee on Psychiatry and Religion of the Central Conference of American Rabbis, reminds us that the Prophet Jeremiah recognized the significance of these counselors by equating their value with the priest and the prophet, when he said: "The torah shall not depart from the priest, nor the words from the prophets, nor counsel from the wise." The wise, or *Chachamim*, as they were called, exercised a healing method for sick souls which was intuitively similar to the techniques of modern therapy. They even anticipated modern psychosomatic medicine by their knowledge that emotional stresses produced bodily ailments and by their understanding that, through the talking out of these troubling tensions, a person could find relief and be restored to health. This was not similar to the confessional booth, nor to faith healing; rather it was a relationship between an individual and a religious personality who acted as a counselor in permitting the individual to talk out, face to face with him, his tensions.

By the beginning of the Christian era the role of the rabbi tended more and more in the direction of education and juridical duties. It was not until 1700 that the biblical role of Chachamim was revived in all its fullness by the Hasidic Rabbis of Eastern Europe.

[53]

Rabbi Kagan points out that these rabbis had remarkable insight into the emotional needs of every person to conquer anxiety and find confidence in life. "Their followers made frequent private visits to them for this help. One hundred fifty years before the introduction of psychoanalysis, one of these Hasidic rabbis said, 'Every person needs one true friend; this friend should be so close to him that he is even able to tell him that of which he is ashamed.'"

The direct effect that Hasidic Judaism had on its adherents along these pastoral lines is by now hard to estimate. According to David Bakan (1958), this strain of Jewish culture was integral to the development of Freudian psychoanalysis. Bakan argues convincingly that it was not by chance that psychoanalysis was introduced by a Jew and flourished best where Jewish influences played a dominant cultural role.

Rabbi Kagan (1959) describes some of the influences that led him to re-emphasize, in his own rabbinate, the role of the rabbi as counselor: the Wisdom Books of the Bible (especially Proverbs and Psalms), the Hasidic movement in Judaism of the eighteenth century, and the great rediscovery about the human soul made by a modern Jew, Sigmund Freud.

It was my study of Sigmund Freud which enabled me to grasp the full meaning of what the Biblical Chachamim and the 18th century Hasidim were doing. Freud was very proud of his Jewish heritage, even though he claimed he was not religious. Despite his agnosticism, Freud did make the greatest contribution to religious thinking in the 20th century by his insistence that people act through unconscious motives. Therefore, if people are to behave according to the high morals and ethics religion requires of them, they must first become aware of those hidden guilts and fears which block them from such behavior. The first clergyman to appreciate Freud's constructive contribution was one of his early students, Oscar Pfister, a Swiss Protestant minister, who applied his new knowledge of psycho-analysis in his pastoral work with his congregation forty years ago. Freud wrote to Pfister:

"In itself, psycho-analysis is neither religious nor the opposite, but an impartial instrument which can serve the clergy as well as the laity when it is used only to free suffering people. I have been struck in realizing that I had never thought of the extraordinary help the psycho-analytical method could be in pastoral work, probably because wicked heretics like myself are far away from that circle."

Rabbi Kagan describes how these three influences combined to bring him a realization of how psychiatry has awakened religion to a new self-understanding: first, by reviving interest in the ancient healing method of classic Judaism, known to it because it was the one ancient religion which did not separate the soul from the body; second, by clarifying and reaffirming the ancient contention of religion that character strength will depend on parent-child relation (illustrated by the many family stories in the Bible); third, by giving scientific demonstration of the claim made by religion that the only road to personal happiness and stability comes from the individual's capacity to be hopeful, and his capacity to love.

Indeed, while psychology has emphasized today the fact that every person's greatest need is the need to be needed, expressed through his need to belong and his need to be loved, it has come around more and more to realize that every person has a need to believe. The absence of any belief in life will even warp the capacity for human love physically as well as psychically.

In former times, this need to believe was met by belonging to homogeneous communities with religious orientation. Today, however, many individuals are constantly moving about in a secularized, disoriented society. They are in search of roots which routine rituals and prayer today seem inadequate to supply. Because many such individuals are hoping to recover their faith through a personal spiritual relationship, they are beginning to welcome the clergyman who emphasizes in his role not so much the ritual or the group symbol, but the counselor who has appropriately trained himself for that role in modern terms.

CHRISTIANITY

In *A History of the Cure of Souls,* John T. McNeill (1951) points out that since the dawn of Christian times, much of the help given to mankind in distress has been prompted by religious motives, and has been carried out under the assumption that fundamental personality problems refuse to be solved outside the realm of religion.

Healing was among the tasks assigned to those first ordained by Christ. Both the Gospels and the early Christian communities emphasized the essential factors in this ability to heal as being fasting, prayer, and love for mankind. According to some ancient writers, the "gift" of healing is withheld entirely from those motivated by pride or an urge for power, and for this reason is very rare.

With the growth of the church, a priesthood and hierarchy emerged with increasing specialization of roles. The tradition of exorcism and healing of souls tended to wane with these changes, and the guiding of souls became a task primarily for those who were responsible for initiating new monks into the monastic orders. Early monasticism expressed profound concern for the flock-at-large, and the history of monastic reforms shows continual re-emphasis on the pastoral responsibilities of the clergy. An overview of the church in the medieval period, however, reveals fewer signs of a healing ministry. The confessional and the sacraments, McNeill makes clear, absorbed what in other periods called for a personal counseling relationship.

In the Reformation era, considerable emphasis on pastoral counseling can be seen. Luther appears not only as a theologian but as a guide of souls and an experienced confessor. McNeill describes Luther's pastoral care of a parishioner, a woman who showed symptoms of what may have been psychosis and who was led by his prayers to confess her sin of pride, and to appeal for divine help, "whereupon she was soothed to rest." Luther's early followers distributed handbooks and other special writings for the ministry to the sick and dying. John Calvin also emphasized the pastoral duties and is said to have been "at heart, more a pastor than a theologian."

In the seventeenth century, the Protestant movement called "Pietism" opposed forms of religion that did not take the individual and his personal problems seriously. Philip J. Spener, a leader of this movement, was outspoken in his criticism of mass private confessions and stressed other means for the "particular dealing with people." He believed in the value of private conversations and home visitations.

The greatest emphasis given to pastoral care in the eighteenth century, according to McNeill, was through the efforts of Gilbert Burnet, Bishop of Salisbury. Bishop Burnet's *Discourse of Pastoral Care* was written in order "to raise the sense of the obligation of the clergy" in pastoral duties.

Cotton Mather, a leader of early American Puritans (in the eighteenth century), recognized the need for what might be called psychosomatic medicine, and, for some cases, urged the cooperation of pastor and physician. Disorders of the mind, he said, bring diseases of the stomach; in such cases, physicians should present to the patient thoughts that are "anodynes" and endeavor to "scatter the clouds and remove the loads with which his mind is oppressed."

Also in this period, Methodist groups in this country often subdivided themselves into "bands" of twelve members each and a class leader, with the aim of "helping each other to work out their salvation." This was a characteristic of many newly-formed Protestant groups: the responsibilities for pastoral care were initially with the laymen and were only later assumed by the clergy.

In the early nineteenth century a revival of the private confession began in Protestantism, particularly in Germany. Klaus Harms of Kiel was one who favored the re-introduction of the confession as a part of a wider activity in pastoral care. Harms proposed that churches maintain a pastor who was not charged with preaching and could devote himself to visiting those who stay away from church. He further proposed courses of training to be given in the universities for those who, like himself, desired to be a "psychic physician."

In the mid-nineteenth century, a Presbyterian minister, Ichabod Spencer, was concerned with the relationship between the organic, psychic, and spiritual states of people. He kept detailed account of his counseling experiences in his journals. Seward Hiltner (1958), in describing Spencer, speaks especially of his "sustaining power"—his patient and supportive visits during times of prolonged crisis.

Theological writing in the latter half of the nineteenth century was one factor that paved the way for the renewal of pastoral counseling in the second quarter of this century. Theology on the continent turned in the direction of putting man first—his needs, his concerns, his potentialities—and speaking only of God as man knows him. The chief exponent of this "anthropocentric" theology was Friedrich Schleiermacher. His dominant note: "Only through further learning about man can we know God."

The "anthropocentric" tendency in theology occurred at about the same time as new movements in the social sciences, the beginnings of psychoanalysis, the sociology of Max Weber, and the field of comparative anthropology. These streams were potential currents of new life for practical theology, one expression of which was the renewal of pastoral counseling.

THE MODERN EMPHASIS

In a survey of theological education in the United States, H. R. Niebuhr, D. D. Williams, and J. Gustafson (1957) point out that the center of interest in the field of pastoral theology today is in the area of "counseling, which includes ministry to people at the point of their anxieties, frustrations, and threats of mental illness . . . The aim is the fusion of scientific understanding with Christian wisdom and concern." In a concluding statement they write: "When one considers the revitalization of much in the theological curriculum today through new emphasis in psychology or pastoral counseling, it must be concluded that a significant new turn in the education of the ministry has been taken."

Some reasons have already been suggested for the increasing importance and specialization of the pastoral counseling role. Seward Hiltner gives four additional reasons. First, there are many more church members than at any time in history, and the clergyman is faced with more personal needs and problems than ever before and a responsibility to help more individuals. Secondly, the knowledge coming from psychology, psychiatry, and anthropology cannot be ignored. Third, without proper understanding and what Dr. Hiltner calls "shepherding," people cannot be led into a deep level of faith, and, if left in the shallow areas, may withdraw altogether from the pastoral reach. Fourth, in an age of "psychological language," the theological tradition is in danger of being neglected as not relevant to modern life and problems.

According to Prof. Paul E. Johnson (1955) of Boston University School of Theology, counseling is an inescapable aspect of the socially defined role of the pastor:

The role of the pastor is not his own invention, but a social creation emerging from what is expected of him. In the United States, more than 50 per cent of the population belong to churches and synagogues, and these people look to pastors for counsel. . . . [The pastor] is expected to stand by them in time of illness and death, to help them meet crises, and to bless them in their times of rejoicing, such as marriage and childbirth. No pastor can escape the role of counselor unless he turns his back upon these requests and denies his vocation. . . . More people are coming for counsel and expecting more knowledge and skill than ever before. This requires of the pastor additional resources for which he turns to psychology and psychiatry, to social work and the science of man to become more competent in counseling.

No single step but a series of interrelated movements has marked the growing specialization in pastoral counseling. The establishment of clinical training centers where clergymen and theological students can work with professionals in the field of mental health has been a phenomenon of the last three decades. This movement has been accompanied by a new emphasis within theological education on the sciences of man. The responsiveness and self-criticism of the churches regarding their needs in the psychological sciences have led in turn to a psychologically more sophisticated clergy. And yet the field of pastoral counseling seems at present to be a kind of "No Man's Land" to either a psychologist or a theologian. The discipline of pastoral counseling vitally needs further theoretical and research orientation before it will be accepted fully by psychologists and psychiatrists on the one hand and theologians on the other.

APPROACHES TO PASTORAL COUNSELING

"The subtle enemy uses gray hairs to deceive the younger men, by a wrongful appeal to their authority . . . and drags them down either into a baneful indifference or to deadly despair."

Thus begins a fourth century account by John Cassian (1894) of an episode which illustrates, no less than does modern clinical experience, an inherent and age-old problem for pastoral counseling: What approach or attitude or technique ought to be employed?

Cassian continues his account:

When this one, who was not the laziest of young men, had gone to an old man, whom we know very well, for the sake of the profit and health of his soul, and had candidly confessed that he was troubled by carnal appetites . . . fancying that he would receive from the old man's words consolation . . . and a cure for the wounds inflicted on him, the old man attacked him with the bitterest reproaches, and called him a miserable and disgraceful creature, and unworthy of the name of monk, while he could be affected by a sin and lust of this character, and instead of helping him so injured him by his reproaches that he dismissed him from his cell in a state of hopeless despair and deadly despondency.

And when he, oppressed with such a sorrow, was plunged in deep thought, no longer how to cure his passion, but how to gratify his lust, the Abbot Apollos, the most skillful of the Elders, met him, and seeing by his looks and gloominess his trouble and the violence of the assault which he was secretly revolving in his heart, asked him the reason of this upset; and when he could not possibly answer the old man's gentle inquiry, the latter began to ask him still more earnestly the reasons for his hidden grief. And by this he was forced to confess that he was on his way to a village to take a wife, leave the monastery and return to the world. . . .

And then the old man smoothed him down with kindly consolation, and told him that he himself was daily tried by the same pricks of desire and lust, and that therefore he ought not to give way to despair, nor be surprised at the violence of the attack of which he would get the better not so much by zealous efforts, as by the mercy and grace of the Lord.

So saying, the elderly Apollos persuaded the young monk to postpone his marital intentions and return to his monastery. Later, according to Cassian, Appollos visited the censorious "counselor" who had precipitated the difficulty. There, in answer to Appolos' prayer, "the Lord caused the old man to suffer the same lusts which had so tormented the younger monk, to the end that he may learn to condescend to the weakness of sufferers, and to sympathize even in his old age with frailties of youth." Interpreting to the old monk the purpose of this torment which had befallen him, Apollos then says, "And so learn from your own experience never to terrify with destructive despair those who are in danger, nor harden them with severe speeches, but rather restore them with gentle and kindly consolations."

This fourth century episode illustrates the perennial conflict between the authoritarian, moralistic, even punitive mode of counseling, and the nonauthoritarian, nondirective, more permissive approach—not to mention the Abbot's highly appropriate and rather witty method of teaching a good clinical lesson.

Fifteen hundred years later religious leaders are still divided as to the best approaches to counseling, and to some extent so is the medical profession; there are equally strong advocates of "directive" and of "nondirective" counseling. Paul E. Johnson (1955) writes that the "authoritarian advice" is one thing which keeps people from coming to their pastors with personal problems:

The traditional methods of counseling used clumsily by the pastor (as well as parents, teachers, and social workers of the old school) are next to futile. They are ordering and forbidding, exhortation and persuasion, abstract logic and intellectual exposition, cheering up and reassurance, use of moral and religious authority.

He concludes that "authoritarian advice" either makes one submissive and dependent upon the adviser, or causes him to reject the advice in order to assert an arbitrary independence.

On the other hand, an equal danger may be the use of the nondirective approach by the clergyman to compensate for—or disguise—a lack of skill or personal conviction. A distinction needs to be made between authoritarianism and authority; there is danger of rejecting the latter along with the former. In the counseling relationship, the parishioner describes his needs, but the minister may have the prior possibility—and responsibility—of defining needs, and may be able to do this with authority but without authoritarianism.

However valuable it may be for the pastoral counselor to maintain "authority" while avoiding "authoritarianism" in the counseling relationship—a technique which Harry Stack Sullivan urged for lay therapists—many clergymen have been influenced by the nondirective or client-centered approach usually associated with the name of Carl Rogers.

In this approach, the counselor structures a relationship that is free from judgmental attitudes or moral censure. Paul Johnson points out that nonjudgmental attitudes are essential to effective counseling. "For as soon as we condemn, we separate the counselee as an outcast, and the therapeutic relationship is broken."

The counselor must allow the counselee to tell his story in his own way, without directing or controlling the conversation. He thus encourages the release of feelings, for as long as they are repressed they continue to interfere with true understanding.

Johnson believes that the term *nondirective* is a misnomer, for there is subtle guidance in every step of Roger's method. "The counselor gives structure to interviews by defining the relationship as permissive. In restating the feelings the counselor selects for emphasis what he considers most significant. Without giving advice the counselor does affirm insights, clarify issues, state alternatives, and encourage positive steps of action when chosen by the counselee." Rogers' method is neither totally directive nor totally nondirective. Rogers himself prefers the term "client-centered," and he has also used the phrase, "responsive-counseling."

Some implications of the term "pastoral" in the phrase "pastoral counseling" have been further clarified by Arthur Becker (1958) of Capitol Theological Seminary in Columbus, Ohio. For his doctoral dissertation at Boston University School of Theology, Becker made an empirical study of the counseling methods of 68 clergymen. One of his major inferences is that while the basic functions of the therapeutic relationship seem to be the same for psychotherapy as for pastoral counseling, there are significant differences in the interpretation and carrying out of these functions:

1. The gratification of the basic needs for a sense of safety, a feeling of belongingness, a sense of worth, were held to be present in all good therapeutic relationships. In pastoral counseling these needs are supplied not only through the counseling relationship but in the person's relationship with God, to which counseling may introduce him or in which it strengthens him.

2. The relationship serves as a corrective experience and model in which previous conflicts are exteriorized; it becomes a proving ground for testing new insights, decisions, and behavior patterns.

3. The relationship is also an occasion for social learning in which the person unlearns defensive patterns, learns new social skills, and

new or enlarged goals and values. In the pastoral counseling relationship, learning also centers around the process of unlearning infantile conceptions of God and learning more mature ones.

THE PROTESTANT ORIENTATION IN COUNSELING

Both Johnson and Becker have discerned some of the distinctions between religious and secular counseling, and in so doing have brought out some of the significance of the term, "pastoral." In order to investigate other differences between these two types of counseling, Jean Blumen and Allan Eister (1958) sent questionnaires to Protestant and Roman Catholic clergymen and social workers and also interviewed them. In the course of their investigation they discerned some differences between Protestant and Roman Catholic approaches as well.

Among Protestants the authors found a strong emphasis on the desirability of a psychiatric approach to counseling. Every minister interviewed stressed the need for training in clinical psychology and for some familiarity with the principles of psychiatry, if only to be better able to recognize problems that lie beyond their competence. The respondents almost unanimously felt that no person was qualified to help in personal problems *solely* because he had been ordained and thereby had become the instrument of special power.

Blumen and Eister pressed their respondents to explain why they felt the obligation to add this secular psychiatric training to their theological preparation. Responses ranged from the feeling that "oftentimes other professional help is inaccessible to parishioners with limited means and the minister is virtually compelled to assume the role of the poor man's psychotherapist," to the recognition that "ministers must be prepared to cope with people for whom other types of counseling have failed and who turn to the minister as their last hope."

In studying the relationship of the clergy to secular counselors, Blumen and Eister compare pastoral counseling with services carried out by social caseworkers rather than by psychologists and psychiatrists. They thus add a valuable dimension to the study of pastoral counseling.

As a group, the authors found, the Protestant clergymen did not express any distinction between pastoral counseling and social work counseling. Moreover, they equated themselves professionally with social workers in counseling, seeing largely the same types of problems in the people who come to them for help, and dealing with them in much the same way. Yet the religious orientation found in pastoral counseling and also its greater impersonality and anonymity seem to have a strong appeal.

THE ROMAN CATHOLIC ORIENTATION

Blumen and Eister (1958) have some useful findings about approaches to pastoral counseling on the part of the Roman Catholic clergy. Their source is the replies to mailed questionnaires, direct interviews with the Catholic clergy, and a series of interviews at a representative Catholic seminary. We summarize their findings here, quoting directly from portions of their study.

The general opinion among the Catholic priests interviewed, the authors found, was that the pastor's role as counselor derived from his intimate relationship to God. It was viewed as an obligation which rests upon him because he uniquely understands the religious implications of human problems. As one respondent explained, "The priest is primarily interested in the religious and spiritual welfare of the person," the implication being that this could be separate from the emotional and psychological states of the individual.

The primary objective in Catholic counseling, it was explained, is to ensure the counselee's fulfillment of his *religious duties,* since it is by these means alone that the individual can be restored to the grace of God which is the essential step in seeking the solution to any personal problem. . . .

The Catholic pastoral counselor's image of himself seems to be both more consistent and more limited than that of the Protestant counselor, consisting as it does, of three fairly well-defined actions:

(1) reminding the counselee of his religious duties, (2) outlining the religious imperatives inherent in the counselee's problem, and (3) referring the counselee to the proper source of further help. Once the priest is assured that he has accomplished the first two of these, he will readily direct the individual to other specialists for socio-economic, psychiatric, medical, or legal help. . . .

Because the Catholic clergyman as counselor feels his appropriate concern is for the individual's religious and spiritual condition . . . he places minimal emphasis on the psychiatric approach and does not seek or receive the intensive psychological and psychiatric training that is considered desirable by the Protestant minister. There is, in fact, no formal course of study in pastoral counseling as such in the Roman Catholic Seminary visited. The rector of the Catholic school described the courses in Pastoral Theology as designed to "acquaint students with the practical problems of the ministry . . . with how to deal with unusual types of people they will meet in their parishes (e.g., people troubled with religious scruples, chronic delinquents, or people whose religious problems are complicated by illness). It presents the principles of sexual amorality and indicates how sexual problems affect the single person and the married couple."

"Problems of insecurity and frustration in a person who is fundamentally normal" was the general type of problem most often cited by Catholic clergymen as being more amenable to pastoral counseling than to social work counseling or psychiatric counseling. The explanation for this was that these problems "involve the religious and moral concepts of an individual" and, therefore, lie clearly within the province of the priest.

While the parish priest is expected to handle "run-of-the-mill" personal problems for his parishioners, people with problems of greater complexity must be directed to other agents within the diocese if possible.

Three main reasons were advanced to support the priest's claims to competence as a counselor for "ordinary" personal problems, viz., (1) the priest is a minister of religion, and religion is an important part of every person's life, involving principles which are fundamental to the human character; (2) the intelligence, education, and professional training of the priest, as well as his experience in coping with human sinfulness, particularly in the course of hearing confessions, fit him to advise people on personal problems; and (3) the position of the priest is one that creates a feeling of confidence and respect.

Asked to comment specifically on the differences in approach between the priest and professional social caseworkers, one respondent declared, "The social worker regards religious and spiritual aspects as a means to an end, whereas the priest regards material and social welfare as a means to the spiritual and religious condition of an individual." Another said, "The social worker must wait until the counselee finds himself so harassed that he seeks professional help. The priest usually deals with these people *before their situation becomes so acute.*"

A major difference, according to another, is that the social worker does not use prayer in his counseling. He explained: "The normal sick person takes it for granted that the priest has come to say a prayer for him, also to administer the sacraments. . . . For a physically well person who seeks the priest's help on a personal problem, the priest will urge him to seek the answer to his problem not just in material sources but through prayer. If a person doesn't ask the priest to pray for him or with him, the priest must suggest it nonetheless, for prayer is a normal, necessary help for anyone in trouble."

THE JEWISH ORIENTATION

In a study of pastoral counseling among American rabbis, Jeshaia Schnitzer (1958) received completed questionnaires from 276 Reform rabbis, 213 Conservative rabbis and 125 Orthodox rabbis. (These 614 respondents are one-fourth of all rabbis with congregations in this country.)

Of the Reform rabbis who responded, 85 per cent indicated that they did pastoral visiting; 90 per cent said they engaged in counseling; 93 per cent replied affirmatively when asked, "Do you think counseling is an essential part of a rabbi's professional duties?";

88 per cent had done some reading on counseling. In follow-up interviews most of the rabbis stressed the importance of counseling. One stated that "counseling must have a *natural* basis for understanding people. It is a gift and the next best thing is experience, and a third is reading." Another said, "One does not get this through courses or schooling, but rather through actual experience in the realm of human relations. Developing the role of counseling takes maturity and growing with the job." Many rabbis were unconcerned about "techniques" for the counseling role. "One cannot use techniques, nor can you move people by techniques . . . the main skill is in your own enthusiasm."

For the Conservative group, 85 per cent said that they made it a rule to do pastoral visiting; 89 per cent stated that they engaged in counseling; and 73 per cent had done reading on counseling. Several rabbis shared a point of view expressed by one respondent thus: "The best teacher is intuition and instinct; therefore, the pastoral or counseling function of a rabbi cannot be acquired through training nor superimposed if there is no natural gift."

Of the 105 Orthodox rabbis who responded to Dr. Schnitzer's questionnaire, 88 per cent said that they make it a rule to do pastoral visiting, and 93 per cent considered counseling an essential part of their profession. A larger percentage among the Orthodox make premarital counseling a rule than do the representatives of the other two groups. Fewer Orthodox rabbis read on the subject of counseling than do members of the other groups. The majority of the Orthodox rabbis insisted that no special training was required for the counseling role. For most of them, "common sense" and "experience" are the only two prerequisites for counseling. One respondent said: "I believe the experience of a rabbi is enough and does not require reading on counseling. One who studies the Talmud and life in general is prepared like the one who reads on counseling."

In a summary statement about his findings, Dr. Schnitzer (1958, p. 144-145) writes:

Though there were so many who have a keen awareness of the importance of human relations and the significance of the counseling role, few rabbis are ready or prepared to accept the implications of the pastoral and counseling role.

The majority of rabbis expressed themselves against special training for the counseling role. . . .

Not many had learned the delicate art of listening which helps greatly to keep out of counseling the projecting "I," "common sense," and "my personal experience." One has to become a listening rather than a talking rabbi to function as a real counselor. . . . The rabbi of the past lived in a world of authoritarianism, while the American rabbi of today lives in a free and democratic society, and he must thus change his approach in working with people.

The "democratic process" of modern counseling, the author believes, supplements rather than opposes the teachings of the Jewish tradition, and will help the American rabbi to implement a dynamic Judaism.

After considering in this chapter some trends in pastoral counseling, in both the Christian and Jewish traditions, we now observe—through the medium of empirical studies—counselor vis-a-vis counselee in the pastoral situation.

V
<hr/>

Counselor and Counselee
in Pastoral Care

In a national study conducted for the Joint Commission on Mental Illness and Health, Gerald Gurin, Joseph Veroff, and Sheila Feld (1960) found that 14 per cent of their 2460 interviewees had gone somewhere for help about emotional or psychological problems at some time in their lives, and 42 per cent of these had gone to the clergy. The rest had gone to social, educational, or mental health agencies, the family physician, or to a psychiatrist or psychologist. The clergy were appealed to more frequently than any other resource for help in time of distress.

One reason for this may be their sheer numerical superiority: 350,000 ordained clergymen, of all faiths, in the United States, 235,000 of them in parish work. Additional reasons for their priority as sources of help may be: they are geographically well located and distributed as resources; there is no charge for their services; there is no such stigma attached to seeing them as that which might be aroused by identifying oneself as in need of *psychiatric* or *psychological* help.

The extent to which the modern emphasis on counseling has been realized at the parish level is reflected by other studies. In one of these, the investigation of local counseling activities by the clergy was part of a country-wide study of nonpsychiatric community resources conducted for the Joint Commission on Mental Illness and Health by Reginald Robinson, David F. De Marche, and Mildred K. Wagle (1960). Out of the more than 3000 counties they had surveyed, they selected fifteen in various sections of the nation in which to interview key individuals regarding helping resources and agencies. Clergymen of all faiths were included among these individuals in each county visited.

No attempt was made to determine the "average" amount of pastoral counseling or the degree to which the "average" clergyman might be rated among a community's non-psychiatric mental health resources. Rather, members of the clergy were selected for interviews on the basis of their known interest and ability in the area of mental health, as well as the degree to which they were active in the community and known to supportive agencies, the goal being to learn to what extent and in what ways the more knowledgeable and interested clergymen were contributing.

Drs. Robinson and DeMarche made available for our study the transcripts of interviews which they conducted in seven communities in widely divergent sections of the country.

In a California county visited in the course of this study there are a total of 25 churches, ranging in size of membership from 130 to 1500, with a median of 400. About 60 per cent of the members are women and 40 per cent men. Most of the churches serve a membership in the middle or upper income group.

Of all the recorded or remembered problems brought by parishioners to the attention of the clergy during the previous year, 45 per cent were marital problems, 17 per cent parent-child conflicts, 10 per cent juvenile problems, 8 per cent problems of the aged, 9 per cent fairly severe mental and emotional disturbances, and 11 per cent alcoholism.

Some clergymen in this area are aware that they cannot act alone in dealing with this many-sided problem. One pastor, with training in the field of mental illness and mental health, counsels quite extensively, but frequently refers parishioners with deep-seated conflicts to other sources of help. It was his feeling that he could "cope with all but a handful" of the mental and emotional problems which came to his attention. Three clergymen have joined with other community agencies to provide counseling services in conjunction with them.

One church in this county set up a six-month pilot program in which a clinically trained chaplain was employed. By the end of the second week, six persons had called for help; and by the end of the third week, counseling sessions were in progress with five persons on the basis of two one-hour sessions a week. By the end of the fourth month, three more persons had come for help, and sessions for those who had begun earlier tapered off to one a week. Five of the counselees continued for the entire six months, receiving about thirty-six hours of counseling each. The program is still in process of evaluation to determine the advisability of conducting similar programs in other churches.

The responses to the interviews in this area would indicate that the clergymen had considerable understanding of mental and emotional problems. Their varied training and experience ranged from twelve semester hours of pastoral counseling and extensive training in psychiatric social work to special training in a State hospital clinic, and 30 units in educational psychology and counseling. Three of the pastors made frequent referrals to such resources as Alcoholics Anonymous, private psychiatrists, family service agencies, medical clinics, and hospitals. Sources of referrals to the pastors themselves included schools, sheriffs' offices, courts, a military base, and family agencies. However, the majority of referrals for counseling were designated as "self-referrals."

In a predominantly rural county in North Carolina, clergymen who were interviewed indicated that they felt a great need for a community mental health clinic, since psychiatric resources were out of reach for most of their parishioners, from the point of view of both distance and expense. The minister of one of the larger churches in this area commented that "counseling is a major part of a minister's work," and that he did as much of it as time permitted. His church had recently employed an assistant pastor with some clinical training experience to share the pastoral visiting and counseling program and to develop group discussions.

This pastor reported that a large portion of his cases centered around the question of separation and divorce. Sometimes his counseling occurred prior to such action, or was sought in order to avoid such action. Other frequent counselees have been divorced persons with problems of readjustment, sometimes with reference to children. The pastor estimated that about 15 members of his church (or 3 per cent of the membership) were at the time in need of psychiatric treatment. Most of his counseling cases, he said, were "self-referrals," but he emphasized that he did not always wait for them to come to him; when he spotted difficulties, he arranged circumstances as often as possible to open a way for the parishioner to start discussion.

Inquiries in a county in Ohio indicated lack of available help in proportion to those who required it. According to one clergyman, many of his colleagues do pastoral counseling even though they are not specifically trained. Referrals are made to Alcoholics Anonymous, family service agencies, and psychiatrists.

A rabbi in this area with considerable training in counseling and a heavy counseling load strongly favored referrals to psychiatrists. He estimated that over half of the people to whom he gave consultation were unable to pay the fees of psychiatrists in private practice. He thought a useful and needed step would be the establishment of an Adult Guidance Center.

In a Pennsylvania county many of the clergy seemed to do much counseling on their own, without many referrals. Among the Protestant ministers interviewed, the bulk of counseling appeared to concern marital problems, which the ministers felt they could handle adequately themselves. The Roman Catholic priest who was interviewed said that, while he never discouraged members from going to social workers and the family service, he never suggested it because "caseworkers can do no more than priests can."

In a rural county in the State of Washington only two clergymen, both Protestant, were found who did any significant amount of counseling. One of these draws counselees from a wide area, only a small proportion of them being his own parishioners. This pastor is careful to recognize his limitations, and he makes considerable use of community resources for referral. He admitted having some difficulty in referring to psychologists and psychiatrists because of reluctance on the part of the person needing help. Most of his cases are marital problems, some parent-child relationships, and a few juvenile problems.

Although he has instituted a case conference series in which various professional sources cooperate in the discussion of particular problems, he strongly feels a need for a mental health clinic in the community.

A pastor in Wyoming reported having 640 consultations in one year on marital problems in his congregation. The few parishioners he sees with severe mental or emotional disturbances he refers to a psychiatrist or to a mental health clinic in a neighboring city. He was emphatic in stating that the community could use a mental health clinic of its own.

In a community in Georgia, a Protestant clergyman reported having about 150 counseling cases a year, approximately one-half centering around marital problems. This minister, despite considerable clinical training, said he hesitates "to put up his shingle," because he knows he will be "swamped."

He described the recent circumstances of referring a parishioner to the nearest psychiatrist for help; the parishioner was now making a 250-mile trip every two weeks for his interviews. For those lacking the time or money to make such trips, he said, "the doctors in the town prescribe a good many tranquilizing drugs."

A considerable number of the clergymen who were interviewed stated that the majority of those who came to them for counseling were from outside their own parish. Their counselees were in some cases members of another church and active in it while coming for counseling, or, in other cases, did not belong to any religious group. More than one pastor indicated that his own parishioners tended to go elsewhere if they sought religious counseling rather than turning to him. The trend in general suggested to these pastors a strong desire for anonymity on the part of the parishioners.

The interviews with clergymen in these counties reflect the impression that considerable numbers of people undoubtedly go to the clergy for help in time of stress; yet nearly all the respondents agreed that many people who need help are either not getting it, or are not getting enough. A large proportion of these clergymen saw the most pressing need in their own communities to be not for stepped-up use of the clergy, not for more pastoral counseling, but for mental health clinics and community centers where trained specialists could offer low-cost assistance to those who need it.

The responses of clergymen in these communities provide some indication of what individual pastors are doing to help persons in stress, either by themselves or in cooperation with other sources of help. Perhaps a useful product of an inquiry of this nature is the kind of questions it prompts one to ask.

What pastors, for example, are likely to make use of an authoritarian approach to the counselee and his problem, and what ones are more likely to use a nondirective, supportive technique? Is it possible to predict from a pastor's theological position, background experience, and the like, which direction he will take? Who is likely to work within a psychological frame of reference and who within a theological? Who tends to refer fairly promptly, and who works with the counselee for an extended period? What use of increased referral sources would the clergy make if they had them?

The quality as well as the number of resources—not to mention their location and accessibility—is a critical factor in their degree of use by the clergy. Is there any relation between the amount and frequency of referral and the attitude, personality, qualifications, and experience of the clergy themselves?

We see such a variety of experiences and approaches to counseling on the part of clergymen in many communities that it would be foolhardy to press for neat answers to any of the foregoing questions. Their complexity is illustrated particularly by the last. When we inquire whether those clergymen with greater psychological sophistication tend to make more or less use of referral to, and cooperation with, psychiatrists and other community resources, psychiatric and nonpsychiatric, the picture is not black and white, but mixed. Some pastors with considerable training and clinical experience are ready to work with any parishioner with any kind of problem, with the exception of the psychotic; others, with equal training and experience, limit their counselees to those with fairly simple problems, usually those of an interpersonal (rather than intrapersonal) nature. For the former, the increased psychological sophistication may give confidence that they can be of help in many kinds of situation. For the latter, the advanced knowledge and experience may prompt early referral in any but the most simple cases. A parallel situation can be observed among those pastors with little training. Some tackle nearly anything, while some use great caution and take on only the most simple problems.

The process—or the moment—of referral is a kind of prism in which is refracted the whole network of the clergyman's relationship with his counselees and with the community as symbolized by its helping resources. Here also are caught and reflected the clergyman's philosophy regarding mental health matters, and his judgment and skill in assessing the severity of a parishioner's problem. As we show later, the answer to this important question of referral, as well as to those regarding type of counseling—authoritative or supportive, theologically or psychologically oriented—would appear to depend more on the personality of the pastor than on the amount of formal training he has had or on the nature of his religious background.

As we turn from an extensive to a more intensive community study, we note that the average amount of counseling done by the clergymen of whom we have acquired any knowledge is surprisingly low. In a research project at Harvard Divinity School, in which the Joint Commission cooperated, Gene Nameche (1958) conducted structured interviews with a stratified random sample of one hundred Protestant clergymen. Nameche found that urban and suburban Protestant ministers, as represented by his interviewees, counsel somewhat less than three hours per week. Rural Protestant clergymen were found to counsel slightly less. Schnitzer (1958) estimates that the Jewish clergy counsel about the same as do their Protestant counterparts—namely, three hours a week for urban and suburban rabbis, and about two hours per week for rural men. These figures would average out to about 2.2 hours of pastoral counseling per week. Over a one year period this amounts to approximately 112 hours of counseling time per clergyman. An estimate based on related data indicates that the average number of counseling sessions for each counselee is four. Thus a clergyman might counsel with 28 different parishioners during the year, giving about four hours to each one.

Is there any relation between a clergyman's theological position and the extent of his counseling? Several investigators have devised scales of religious attitudes for both laymen and clergymen. Because most religious groups, and especially Protestant denominations, are too heterogeneous to use as a key to a person's religious position along a conservative-liberal line, such scales are sometimes extremely useful. Nameche (1958) devised a simple scale of this type for clergymen involved in counseling. The Protestant ministers who were interviewed were divided into three theological categories, based on their responses: conservative, moderate, and liberal. The moderate Protestant group did by far the most counseling; the liberals were second; and the more conservative pastors (including fundamentalists) did the least.

About 60 per cent of the clergymen interviewed counsel less than two hours per week, depending on a kind of common-sense psychology. These men may have had one or two general psychology courses, usually in college rather than in the seminary, but they are usually unfamiliar with abnormal and counseling psychology. (It is estimated that less than 10 per cent of the country's clergymen have received clinical pastoral training or its equivalent in psychology or counseling.)

A third of the clergymen counsel between two and nine hours per week; many of these have received their training in psychology at the seminary level.

The last seven per cent of the clergymen, mostly theologically "moderate," spend from ten to twenty-two hours a week doing counseling, and usually have had graduate training in clinical or social (not pastoral) psychology. Many are trained at least to the Master's Degree level in psychology; some have doctorates in psychology, others in pastoral psychology. The greater part of pastoral counseling, it would appear, is done by a comparatively small number of clergymen.

In a series of structured interviews with 75 counselees of clergy-men in a large metropolitan area, Nameche (1959) found that twice as many women as men had sought help from the clergy. The difference remained significant even after controlling for the fact that there were more women than men in the congregations of all the clergymen concerned. Where marital discord is the cause of seeking pastoral counseling, it is more likely to be the wife who comes to the clergyman, and only after considerable persuasion does the husband enter a counseling relationship.

The young adult age group (eighteen through thirty-five) received a disproportionately large amount of counseling compared with the upper age groups. Although clergymen counsel more members over thirty-five years old than any other age group, the adult population of the churches is greater than either the youth or young adult groups; hence the young adult group receives proportionately more counseling than either of the other two age groups.

Generally little difference was observed in terms of educational level between those who sought pastoral counseling and those who did not. The difference was in the direction of counselees having a slightly higher educational level than the uncounseled members of the parish. College graduates tended to be higher in their use of both psychiatric resources and the clergy.

Roughly half of the counselees interviewed were married, 30 per cent single, and 20 per cent divorced or widowed. This last group was considerably larger than its occurrence in the average congregation.

Individuals who had been to their clergymen for counseling were no more active in church affairs than the average parishioner. Thus, contrary to many church members' expectations, it would appear that one does not need a long record of church activity, involvement, and "faithfulness" to call on his pastor for personal help in time of distress. In fact, in terms of daily religious activity, the counselees interviewed were considerably *less* active than the average non-counseled parishioner. Counselees of ministers seemed to be no more "pious" than laymen who don't go for counseling. Whether persons who are less active in church affairs, less involved with the church, less "faithful," less "pious" need—and receive—more pastoral counseling cannot, of course, be established from these data.

What ministers tend to be singled out for counseling? Of 100 pastors interviewed, the ones proportionately most frequently sought for counseling tend to be those of lower middle class churches, "moderate" theologically, preachers of personally relevant sermons, well-trained in psychology and counseling, and in the middle age group of their profession, with an understanding of counseling from both theological and psychological perspectives. When "pastoral counselees" were asked how they happened to select a particular clergyman for counseling, they often reported that they went because it was part of their own minister's job to counsel his congregants, rather than referring to a pastor's personal characteristics or professional qualifications. When asked how they would choose a pastoral counselor if another counseling problem arose, the counselees simply said that they would go to their own clergyman or one they knew personally—making no mention of personality attributes or even stipulating that their counselor should have had training in the counseling function. (Only three respondents referred to training as a criterion.) Although persons who have had pastoral counseling do not mention personality factors as a basis for deciding whether to go for help or not, whether to go to a clergyman or to a psychiatrist, and which pastor to go to, it would seem that the personality of the clergyman may operate on a more covert level in determining their choice.

It would appear that parishioners in distress do not tend to be highly selective about whom they choose for help. They go to the nearest concerned person who might have had some previous knowledge or experience with the type of problem they face, and thus known to be interested and available. Less than one counselee in five expects professional help in the nature of therapy from his minister. The rest simply "need someone to talk to." What seemed to matter most was that the clergyman was *concerned*. This reflects the finding of Gurin *et al.*, (1960) that persons who go to members of the clergy for help in time of trouble value the contact more for the comfort they derived than for any "cure" for their distress.

Why do many people *not* go to ministers for counseling? The major reservations offered by those who had never gone to a clergyman for help were: "Ministers are too moralistic and I couldn't talk to them: You'd get more hell than help; ministers don't know anything about counseling people; I just wouldn't want anyone to find out I had those kinds of problems." The moralism reason was the one most dominant for counseled and uncounseled parishioners alike, though the former almost consistently reported that early in counseling this fear was dispelled. The last reason, social reserve, seemed to be the strongest deterrent for persons who had no knowledge of pastoral counseling. Further reasons for the existence of a barrier between pastoral counselor and potential counselee are taken up in the following chapter.

In the study that we described earlier, Nameche (1958) distinguished seven broad categories of counseling problems that appeared most frequently among the clergymen he interviewed: marriage and family, youth behavior, psychological distress, alcoholism, problems of illness and aging, vocational and occupational problems, and religious or spiritual questions. Marriage and family problems and psychological distress problems were those most frequently brought to the respondents. These two areas constitute about 65 per cent of all problems brought to the clergymen interviewed. Youth behavior problems—usually worked out between clergymen and parents and only infrequently with the child involved—were third in frequency; problems of illness and aging, fourth; alcoholism, fifth; religious and spiritual questions, sixth; and vocational-occupational problems, seventh.

Only between 6 and 9 per cent of all counseling problems were directly concerned with "religious or spiritual" matters. The minister seems to be less a counselor on religious matters, in the narrow sense of the term, than a kind of "lay counselor" who only infrequently is consulted on problems of a purely religious nature. He is a religious specialist more because he operates within a religious institution than because his counseling work is specialized on religious matters.

But this is how these pastors would have it; they welcome the movement from the domain of religion-in-the-narrow-sense, and into the secular areas of life in order to bring out what Tillich has called the "religious dimension that underlies all of life." Sometimes psychiatrists, psychologists, and social workers do not readily grasp this intention of many clergymen, and therefore criticize them for crossing professional boundaries.

An attempt not to cross professional boundaries but to make the professional resources of the community more readily available to the parishioner in need of help is reflected in the growth of pastoral counseling centers. This movement we consider in the following chapter.

VI

Pastoral Counseling Centers

Most of the 235,000 active clergymen in the country engage in pastoral counseling, at some time and to some degree, whether or not they have had specialized training. Most have not; only an estimated 8000 clergymen have had some form of clinical pastoral education during theological school or since ordination.

Supplementing the contribution of pastoral counseling to the needs of troubled people are several specialized forms of the ministry. Some of these, such as the mental hospital chaplaincy discussed in the first chapter, serve special groups; others channel and focus the resources of pastoral counseling in a more personalized way than the activities of the individual clergyman, and in addition make available the services of mental health specialists—psychiatrists, psychologists and others—under religious auspices. An example of the latter is the pastoral counseling center, designed to serve the needs of the troubled more specifically than those of the ill.

The pastoral counseling center is a recent attempt by the Protestant churches to meet spiritual and mental health needs in areas and ways in which the church now feels it can effectively function. Help with personal and family problems has long been made available by Jewish and Roman Catholic groups through their many excellent Family Service and Welfare agencies. But the pastoral counseling centers with which we are concerned here are a recent development, and, as far as we have been able to learn, have been established only under Protestant auspices.

We know of only 73 pastoral counseling centers in the country. Rather than make a generalized and theoretical description, we will first describe three specific centers—one connected with a theological school and university, one with large staff of both clergy and psychiatrists and a heavy client load, and a small program conducted by a single church.

An interdenominational counseling service has been conducted for seven years by Boston University School of Theology. Members of the Advisory Board include psychiatrists, pastoral counselors, professors of theology, business men, and others. The staff includes nine ordained pastoral counselors, all of whom have completed clinical training and are accredited by the Institute of Pastoral Care or the Council for Clinical Training. In addition there are about 20 student counselors under supervision. Serving as consultants are a psychiatrist, an educational psychologist, a clinical psychologist, and a social worker from the Family Service Association. During the first five years, 1221 persons were given a total of 6202 interviews. Sixty-five per cent of the clients continued in counseling beyond the first interview.

The counseling service makes the following classification of problems seen in the 198 persons served in one year: 86 with marital problems; 28 with problems of personal growth; 24 with child-parent relationship problems; 16 with anxiety and guilt problems; 13 with psychoses; 9 with vocational problems; 7 with academic problems; 7 with health problems; 4 with sex problems; and a few with socioeconomic, grief, or theological problems. "We may wonder why theological problems are not more frequent in pastoral counseling," the 1957 Annual Report observes. "Actually, theology is a frame of reference for all of the counseling. But the presenting problems are naturally human problems which occasion the search for perspective. It is in later developments of counseling, as the conversation moves into consideration of perspectives, that theology is more often discussed."

During one year, 45.5 per cent of the incoming referrals were from pastors; 27 per cent were self-referrals; 10.5 per cent were referred by friends and relatives; 7 per cent were referred by university personnel; 3.5 per cent by physicians; and 5 per cent by social agencies. Only 6 per cent were by the School of Theology and

Chapel staff. These figures reflect the broad availability and use of the Counseling Service by the community at large.

The Service provides a number of graduate courses, several of them in affiliation with general and mental hospitals; a full-time clinical pastoral training course is conducted during the summers. Programs lead to the Master's and Doctor's degrees in theology. Annual workshops in pastoral counseling are also held, usually attended by 200 or more clergymen, physicians, psychiatrists, social workers, and nurses. These include lectures by pastoral counseling leaders and seminars for group discussion.

The Annual Report for 1957 pointed out the following chief concerns requiring further study and action:

First, there is need to define more precisely the role of the pastoral counselor, the goals and methods of his counseling, and his relation to other helping professions.

Second, there is concern over the chronic waiting list among those who ask for counseling. The strategic moment is when counseling is most urgently desired, and to delay beyond that time is to suffer loss of maturation and effective response to the need.

Third, there is the question of the optimum length for a series of interviews. It is recognized that each situation is unique and the counselor must be guided by the individual need of the person before him. Yet we must consider the terminal procedures.

Fourth, there is the recurring question of charging fees for counseling. Is this motivation needed to control the length of series of interviews and to bring a more serious effort to reach the goals of the counseling?

Fifth, there are questions on how best to fulfill the educational responsibility to prepare pastoral counselors who are competent to meet human needs effectively.

Such questions as these would seem to apply to the whole range of pastoral counseling.

The country's largest and oldest pastoral counseling center is The American Foundation of Religion and Psychiatry, Inc., in New York City. There are nine pastoral counselors, fifteen psychiatrists, five counseling psychologists, two clinical psychologists, two psychiatric social workers, and an administrative staff of six. The Foundation provides an out-patient clinic for the analysis and treatment of emotional and mental disabilities, and provides postgraduate training for ministers, doctors, psychologists, and social workers.

The Clinic got under way in 1937, when Dr. Norman Vincent Peale and Dr. Smiley Blanton began working as a "religio-psychiatric team." The staff was extended to include psychologists and psychiatric social workers, and for 14 years the Clinic was associated with the Marble Collegiate Church, of which Dr. Peale is pastor. In 1951, it was incorporated as a nondenominational clinic. Since 1956 the Bureau of Applied Social Research at Columbia University has conducted intensive research at the Clinic, with the object of evaluating the Clinic's procedures. The Clinic is licensed by the State of New York's Department of Mental Hygiene and approved by the Department of Social Welfare, and receives an annual grant from the New York City Community Mental Health Board. The training center is accredited by the Council for Clinical Training for postgraduate clinical pastoral education.

During the first 20 years, the Clinic counseled approximately 10,000 persons, the professional staff giving over 50,000 hours. In 1951, 2400 counseling sessions were held, and 6100 in 1957. There were 6000 applicants for counseling in 1957, and a large number of these were found to have problems requiring long-term therapy or other needs outside the service area of the Clinic; in these cases referrals were made. New applicants accepted actually numbered 912 for that year. Of the 6100 hours devoted to these during one year, 60 per cent were conducted by pastoral counselors and 40 per cent by psychiatrists, psychologists, and psychiatric social workers. The staff is divided into treatment teams, so that each applicant's problem is viewed by a group of five counselors. As is the case with other clinics, one of the problems cited in the counseling program here is the "waiting period" before applicants who are accepted can begin treatment.

The Clinic offers three programs for training student ministers: (1) post-graduate internships involving one year in residence and participation in supervised counseling and staff activities; (2) introductory 12-week courses, set up in cooperation with the Council for Clinical Training, offering supervised counseling, study, and discussion (recently, a graduate seminar has been added to this program, with meetings one morning a week for 40 weeks); and (3) summer conferences, comprised of one week of lectures, discussion groups, and workshops for pastors and students. The Clinic also holds weekly community conferences open to all clergy in the area, to which pastors are invited to bring their pastoral counseling problems for discussion and guidance.

The research program of the Foundation, under the direction of Dr. Samuel Klausner, has done extensive evaluation and study, especially on the problems of role differentiation between ministers and psychiatrists in a "clinical-pastoral" setting, intake services for the clients, and follow-up of counselees.

A counselor whom we interviewed at a counseling center sponsored by a 1200-member church was a trained psychologist as well as a minister. During 1958, he had dealt with 72 counselees, who had made an average of 12 visits each. His usual weekly load was 9. All the 72 were severe psychoneurotic or near-psychotic cases, who had been referred to him by the clergy of the church or other local clergy and psychiatrists. Most came from the city area; some were commuters. Only three had become church members after counseling. He had a nine-months' waiting list.

Eleven of the counselees had been referred to five associates—local clergymen with considerable training, one being a physician. Those needing supportive therapy were sent to a psychiatrist. The counselor had made referrals to two psychiatrists and to one obstetrician. As an example of referral to the latter, he mentioned a woman who for many years had suffered from fears, anxieties, and misconceptions about sex.

The church's three ministers also carried a heavy counseling load, their province being personal and religious problems, marital counseling, and alcoholism. In the latter problem, they provide a "first-aid" service, and later refer the counselees to Alcoholics Anonymous, or other outside help.

The patients were 60 per cent women and 40 per cent men, most reflecting a rather high socioeconomic and educational level. Many had college degrees and some had postgraduate degrees. In dealing with women, the counselor found frequently that he seemed to be the only one who would listen to them and respect, not reject them.

Problems tended to be presented in one of two ways. Either the counselee had a specific idea of what was troubling him (which might or might not be related to the real difficulty), or he was extremely vague. Many counselees, over the previous five years, had been unable to find anyone with whom they could communicate. They would say, "There's no one I can talk to." This complaint was made especially by ministers' wives, who represented a large proportion of the counselees. The need to communicate—or the lack of communication—had become pathological.

The counselor interpreted some of the symbolic meanings of his role as that of a husband, a father, or a "second self." Not only were the counselees hungry for someone to talk to, but they had to relate to someone in order to feel accepted. Many of them had developed such an unconscious sense of failure that they had to be reassured that the things which had happened had not been their fault. Among men, the most frequent and pressing difficulties seemed to be related to a lack of a sense of direction. Most male counselees were over forty years of age, and had for some time been suffering from a loss—or realization of a lack—of meaning in their lives.

As we have pointed out, the establishment and growth of counseling centers or services is a recent phenomenon within Protestantism. As the clergy have availed themselves of specialized training in counseling theory and techniques, in clinical training experiences at mental and general hospitals, and in clinical and counseling internships of various types, a corps of concerned and qualified counselors has emerged within the ministry. At the same time an increasing awareness of the problems and needs of people, often beyond the counseling abilities of the pastor and usually beyond the time that the busy pastor could conscientiously allot to one situation, suggested the organization of "counseling centers" sponsored by the church, denomination, or council of churches.

In a recent study of pastoral counseling centers, Berkeley Hathorne, Th.D. (1960), has attempted to answer such questions as the following: What is a pastoral counseling center? How did they evolve? How many centers are there in the United States at the present time and where are they located? Under whose auspices are these centers operated? Who are the counselors? What are their qualifications, training and experience? What type of counseling is practiced in these centers? What types of cases handled? What affiliation do these centers have with other agencies and with other professional persons for referrals, consultations, etc.?

Dr. Hathorne has prepared for us the following findings from his study, the research for which provided the basis of his doctoral dissertation at Boston University School of Theology. His primary data were accumulated by means of a structured questionnaire. Every counseling center that it was possible to locate was contacted by mail, some by personal visit. (Locations of the centers were ascertained by corresponding with church officials throughout the country.)

Seventy-three pastoral counseling centers, located in 24 states and the District of Columbia, are included in Dr. Hathorne's compilation (see Appendix I for the full list). Our discussion and statistical summaries in this chapter are limited to the 48 centers which sent data in time for tabulation. Of the 48, 15 are located in the northeast, 14 in the north central section, 6 in the southeast, 5 in the south central section, and 8 in the southwest. The distribution by geographical regions and states indicates that pastoral counseling centers are not a phenomenon of merely one section of the country. The most striking fact is that the majority are located primarily in the larger urban communities; only one center is in a town with less than 10,000 inhabitants. Forty-three are located in cities with a population of over 50,000 and 20 are in principal cities with populations larger than 500,000. They thus tend to be a large-city phenomenon.

Although many types of church-sponsored social agencies and clinics have been serving for many years, some for half a century, and providing various kinds of counseling, the type of psychologically oriented counseling center now on the American scene is of rather recent date. This new type of center goes by a great variety of names, but all of them have one thing in common: a formally organized counseling program employing the insights of modern psychotherapy to help individuals meet personal and family problems creatively. The first such center sponsored by a Protestant Church was the Religio-Psychiatric Clinic of the Marble Collegiate Church in New York City, which we have described earlier.

In the meantime many other experiments in church counseling clinics were attempted. Most of these were short-lived, usually for want of properly trained counselors and financial backing. The pastoral counseling centers developed principally during the past decade. Half of the centers included in this study were not in existence five years ago, and 39 of the 48 have been organized during the last ten years.

A majority of the centers have been established under the auspices of a single church or denominational organization, with individual churches accounting for over a third of the total. Local interdenominational councils of churches have taken responsibility for nine of the centers; an equal number have been sponsored privately. Six of the centers studied operate under the auspices of hospitals and schools. One was set up by a major tobacco company.

The measure of competence of counselors is difficult to ascertain; however, academic preparation, clinical training, and professional experience are valid indications of qualifications. Thirty-six centers reported in detail the qualifications of the counselors, including degrees, clinical training, professional affiliations and experience. A total of 153 counselors are associated with the 36 centers: 101 ordained clergymen, 17 psychiatrists, 16 clinical and educational psychologists, 18 social workers (most psychiatrically trained), and one gynecologist. Thirty-seven of the centers are directed by clergymen, three by psychiatrists, and two by social workers. Seven of the directors are or have been hospital chaplains. Six are or have been professors of pastoral psychology and counseling.

TYPES AND EXAMPLES OF CENTERS

The church-sponsored counseling centers have in most cases developed independently of one another, so that various types of organizations have evolved. The distinct features of each type can be presented best by specific examples of centers. The following three types of centers will be illustrated, as will sub-types of each category: Pastoral counseling centers without clergy (5); interprofessional pastoral counseling centers (11); and clerical counseling centers (32).

PASTORAL COUNSELING CENTERS WITHOUT CLERGY

Two types of pastoral counseling centers do not include ordained clergy on their counseling staff. The first type, of which two were found, is a psychiatric clinic sponsored by a church: the second type, of which three were found, is a counseling service sponsored by a church. Two Methodist churches in Los Angeles provide examples of both types.

In four years the Mental Health Clinic of the Westwood Community Methodist Church, Los Angeles, has grown from a volunteer staff of three to its present staff of forty-two workers, including psychiatrists, psychologists, and social workers. Although the three ministers of the church are not on the staff of the clinic, they all do considerable independent counseling. However, the clergy and the clinic are entirely separate. As one of the staff members explained, "They (the clergy) often refer cases to the clinic and the clinic refers cases to the ministers, but we do not have direct staff relationships." The staff of this mental health clinic represents three disciplines: psychiatry, clinical psychology, and social work. The director is a psychiatrist.

Only individuals with a monthly income of less than $600 are admitted. Each patient (the term the clinic employs) is expected to make a regular contribution. The fees are based on ability to pay, following a sliding scale which includes consideration of total family income as well as the number of dependents.

This mental health clinic offers many kinds of help to those in emotional distress—primarily those with moderate to severe neuroses. The methods used include "a planned program of preventive therapy, individual therapy, group therapy, play therapy, psychological testing, vocational and educational counseling, and other established methods."

Counseling Service

Several of the church counseling centers have developed from church social service agencies, most of them oriented in social work techniques until recently.

The Church Service Bureau of the First Methodist Church of Los Angeles was begun during the depression of the 1930's as a welfare organization. In 1953 a Counseling Service was added to supplement the other functions of the Bureau. Three trained counselors are employed, none of them clergy.

This counseling service came into being when the staff "realized the most important task was not welfare but to help others to help themselves." Now an average of more than 48 individuals are counseled every month for a total of more than 140 hours. All of these counselees are unable to afford the usual fees required by psychiatrists and psychologists. (Most of them contribute something for this service—an average of $3 per hour.) One-fourth of the individuals who come for counseling require only one to four one-hour interviews—one-fourth require from five to nineteen interviews, and half require more than twenty interviews. Most of these latter long-term cases involve marital adjustments or personality difficulties.

The counseling service has affiliations with psychiatrists and community agencies for referrals. Approximately 2 per cent of the clients are referred to psychiatrists; a large number are referred to various welfare agencies for appropriate assistance.

INTERPROFESSIONAL PASTORAL COUNSELING CENTERS

The relationship of religion and health has been explored and in some cases strengthened during the past quarter century by a number of interprofessional associations and activities. One of the earliest of these was the "religio-psychiatric team," seeking to bring the disciplines of both religion and psychiatry to bear upon the problems of mental health.

The American Foundation of Religion and Psychiatry is the leading example of an interprofessional pastoral counseling center and has been described earlier. Eleven of the responding centers reported four types of interprofessional counseling staffs: clergy and psychiatrists (1), clergy and physicians (1), clergy and psychiatric social workers (5), and combinations of three or more of these (4).

CLERICAL COUNSELING CENTERS

In a total of 32 of the pastoral counseling centers, ordained clergymen are the only counselors. For this reason we have called centers of this type "clerical counseling centers." We can further categorize them by organizational differences.

Centers Sponsored by Individual Churches

Twelve of the 32 clerical counseling centers have been sponsored by individual churches. Typical of these is the Pastoral Counseling Service of the Trinity Baptist Church, San Antonio, Texas. Sensing the need to offer more extensive counseling in a church of 3500 members than could be accomplished by the ministerial staff, the church engaged the services of a competently trained pastoral counselor, who handles all of the counseling himself, an average of 35 hours each week. The center emphasizes short-term counseling (98 per cent of the individuals are interviewed less than ten hours), and specializes in marital and personal problems.

Denominational Clerical Counseling Centers

A large-scale project of establishing clerical counseling centers has been undertaken by the Methodist Church in the State of Indiana. This program was formally started in August 1957 by the Rev. James E. Doty, Area Director of Pastoral Care and Counseling. This program in Indiana is underwritten by the three Annual Conferences in the state, and supervised by an Area Board of Pastoral Care and Counseling. The projected plan is to establish ten regional pastoral care and counseling centers to serve persons living within a fifty mile radius. Several such centers are now in operation.

Typical of these centers is the Indianapolis Pastoral Care and

Counseling Center which began operation in October 1958. The center is housed in North Methodist Church, with the church secretary assuming responsibility for the scheduling of appointments. Five Methodist ministers, with extensive clinical and pastoral experience, serve as the pastoral counselors. Each counselor serves one afternoon or one evening per week. A group of seven consultants, from the fields of psychiatry, psychology, social work, law, and general medicine, meet regularly with the staff of counselors, and are available individually when consultation is needed. An Advisory Board has responsibility for the operation of the center, including the procurement of counselors and consultants if vacancies occur. Although this network of clerical counseling centers in Indiana is sponsored by the Methodist Church, the service is available to non-Methodists as well.

A considerable number of parish clergymen, and members of their families as well, are making use of the counseling services. Most of these persons come for personal counseling on their own initiative; however, some come at the suggestion of their superintendents.

Interdenominational Clerical Counseling Centers

Six of the clerical counseling centers are sponsored cooperatively by interdenominational councils of churches.

Prompted by a need for a marital counseling agency under church auspices, the Metropolitan Church Federation of Greater St. Louis (composed of more than 1000 Protestant churches) organized a counseling center in September, 1954, in a centrally located church. Robert B. Deitchman, M.D. (1957, p. 209), has written a comprehensive report on this center, whose outstanding feature is that it is staffed entirely with voluntary workers, now totaling more than twenty, including clergy-counselors, psychiatric consultants, and personnel for administrative and clerical duties. Only members of the clergy serve as counselors.

The minister-counselors were initially envisaged as those who had completed one or more years of pastoral instruction (under the leadership of chaplains and psychiatrists enlisted by the Committee on Religion and Health of the Church Federation). Generally this is the group who comprise the working minister-counselors but in the community many ministers have had some training or experience in this field. The center has served as an opportunity for post-graduate internship type of training. Because the center serves the community as well as a ministerial counseling training center, qualified . . . minister-counselors in the community serve from time to time upon call from the office of the Administrative Director.

The St. Louis Center makes extensive use of the specialized abilities of volunteer psychiatrist-consultants. Every week a staff conference is held, presided over by a minister appointed for three-month periods by the Metropolitan Church Federation. The psychiatrist functions as an advisor at these staff conferences. All cases are reviewed at the staff meeting, and, if the psychiatrist considers a case to require medical or psychiatric treatment, appropriate referral is made. The psychiatrist-consultant also assists the minister-counselor in understanding the implications of the material presented in the counseling interview, and suggests the direction of future counseling sessions.

The consulting psychiatrist used, as a differentiation between the need for treatment and counseling, an empirical rule that "therapy was that form of treatment required by those individuals who were emotionally disturbed and considered ill; counseling as that guidance that may and perhaps well should be within the framework of faith, giving to the individual assistance in revising certain behavior patterns for more successful adaptation." (Deitchman, p. 212.)

An evaluation of the first 200 cases handled by the center revealed that 56 per cent (112) were concerned primarily with marital problems. Other problems included "nervousness and tension" (10 per cent), "behavior which was disturbing to the community" (7 per cent), alcoholism (5 per cent), and various other problems relating to "the making of decisions and the general conduct of life." Thirty-two of these first 200 cases were referred to private psychiatrists or psychiatric clinics (16 per cent).

Privately Sponsored Clerical Counseling Centers

Eight of the centers where ministers function as counselors are sponsored by other than an individual church, denomination, or council of churches. These independent centers are under the auspices of some institution, such as a theological school or hospital, or of a secular institution such as an industry, or of clergymen working independently of their own church or denomination. Three of these centers are located at educational institutions concerned primarily with the training of counselors. Another three have developed out of chaplaincy work at hospitals. One is unique in that a private industry has employed a clergyman to serve as a counselor for the employees. Five are independent of any church or other social institution, but are nonetheless counseling centers where ordained clergymen provide help for distressed persons.

An outstanding example of a center sponsored by an institution of higher learning is the Pastoral Counseling Service at Boston University School of Theology. This counseling service opened in 1952 under the direction of Professor Paul E. Johnson; it is described earlier in this section in some detail.

TYPE OF COUNSELING AND CASES

All the pastoral counseling centers studied employ a wide variety of counseling techniques and approaches. The chief difference in technique observable between the centers and individual counselors seems to be the depth to which the counseling seeks to go. A few centers, psychiatrically oriented, probe deeply in the process; most counselors employ a type of reflective, client-centered counseling in order to stimulate personal insights into the personality dynamics involved. Without exception, every center reports that it differentiates those cases that need the guidance of a competent psychiatrist and makes the appropriate referral.

SUMMARY

1. The pastoral counseling centers, a movement primarily within the Protestant churches, and still limited in extent, demonstrate an effective way in which the church can make its own resources—and other help as well—available to people in need. They could be at

least a partial answer to the need for substitutes for mental health facilities in small communities. However, the centers have been established not in the small communities where other facilities are lacking, but rather in larger communities, where they supplement, rather than substitute for, other mental health resources.

2. One of the most frequently met criticisms of the counseling center is that a formal center separates or compartmentalizes a function of the ministry, and has led to overspecialization in one aspect of the ministry, when the clergy should be emphasizing a "total ministry." Some critics warn that it is the task of every minister to counsel, and a mistake to set up centers for a task that is the responsibility of every ordained clergyman. While it is true that counseling is a function of every clergyman, all do not have the same gifts for it. The church counseling centers, in attempting to meet the mental and spiritual needs of people, seem to be the best way, organizationally, to make this aspect of the ministry available to the people who need it.

3. The pastoral counseling centers, though limited in number, have fostered cooperation between psychiatry and religion, and challenged both disciplines to discover better ways to work together for the relief of personal problems that might evolve into serious disorders. The centers have provided one further point of intersection for religion and medicine.

4. The counseling centers, while established by churches, have confronted the churches themselves with the challenge to extend the ministry of pastoral care to all of life, to emphasize the wholeness of personality, and to minister to the needs of people, with greater depth and understanding.

5. The pastoral counseling centers have performed a valuable service by acting as a screening agency. Some persons in difficulty may go more readily to a church center than, for example, to a psychiatrist. The pastoral counseling center can then make referrals to other professional resources.

6. The pastoral counseling centers have established a practical method of providing advanced clinical training not divorced from the typical parish situation. Heretofore, most opportunities for train-

ing were in hospital settings. While this type of clinical experience is of undoubted value, it does not provide training in such areas as marriage and family problems.

7. Finally, the pastoral counseling centers have demonstrated another way in which interdenominational cooperation can work in local communities.

VII

Mental Health Aspects of Theological Education

DEALING DIRECTLY with persons who are troubled is by no means the sole extent or even the main focus of the clergyman's work. And other aspects of his work may have important implications for mental health. It is appropriate here to inquire about the training that clergymen have taken—and that future clergymen will take— in preparation for the ministry, the priesthood, and the rabbinate.

Of the 103,224,954 members of all religious groups, 58 per cent (or 35.9 per cent of the total population) are Protestant, 33 per cent (or 20.7 per cent of the total population) are Roman Catholic, 5 per cent (3.3 per cent of the total population) are Jewish, and 3 per cent are Eastern Orthodox. (One per cent are Buddhist, Old Catholic, and Polish National Catholic.) The nationwide average of members per individual church or synagogue: 334. The trend in membership can be seen from statistics that show that, in 1900, 36 per cent of the total population were church members; in 1930, 48 per cent, and in 1957, 62 per cent. (These figures are, however, subject to considerable error since methods of counting members vary from group to group and from time to time.) A related statistic shows an increase related to the population growth. From 1955 to 1956, the total church membership increased 3 per cent (Protestants, up 2.9 per cent, Roman Catholics, up 3.5 per cent), while the population increased 1.7 per cent.

Ministering to these church and synagogue members, and to many nonmembers as well, were 235,100 clergymen at the end of the calendar year 1956, according to the *Yearbook of American Churches* (Landis, 1957). (An additional 114,700 clergymen without charges brought the total of ordained persons to 349,800.) Distributed among 281,687 churches, 214,962 Protestant ministers served 60,148,980 members; 15,851 Roman Catholic priests served 34,563,851 members of 21,121 churches; 2902 rabbis served 5,500,000 members of 4079 temples; 1114 Eastern Orthodox priests served 2,598,055 members of 1425 churches. The remainder were Old Catholic, Polish National Catholic, and Buddhist.

The *Catholic Directory* of 1959 reports an increase in the ranks of the clergy over the figures we have given for 1956. (We have no statistics of Protestant and Jewish clergy for the comparable year.) In 113 dioceses 31,961 diocesan priests served 16,753 parishes. There were 20,728 ordained members of religious orders, a total of 52,689 priests compared with 42,334 a decade earlier. Among the Roman Catholic clergy were counted four cardinals, 33 archbishops, 187 bishops, and 40 abbots. Often ignored in a tabulation of personnel resources were also two significant groups: 9709 Brothers and 164,922 Sisters.

Yet the total for the clergy of all faiths shows a slight decrease proportionate to the population when viewed over a long period of time. In 1850 the ratio of clergy to population was 1.16 per thousand. A hundred years later, in 1950, the ratio was 1.12 per thousand. Today serious shortages exist. The Roman Catholic church has called for measures to attract more men into the priesthood to offset the recent decline in seminary registration. There are 15,000 vacant Protestant pulpits. Some of these vacancies are, of course, related to shifts of population and sometimes to the fact that many communities can no longer support a multiplicity of churches representing several denominations. But some closed churches reflect a true shortage. This is illustrated by the fact that 40 per cent of the pulpits of one large denomination are filled by men from other denominations. The shortage is even more striking when we compare clergymen with another helping profession, physicians. There is a pressing need for more than the present 218,000 physicians in the country, a need not being met by the one-to-thirty ratio of medical school graduates to practicing physicians. The ratio of seminary graduates to practicing clergymen is one to 50; and if we count all ordained persons, the ratio is one to 70.

Compared with the 235,000 clergymen with parishes or other active charges, the number of professional personnel who customarily deal with persons who are to a greater or less degree emotionally disturbed is small. To refer only to two such groups: there are 11,000 psychiatrists and 16,000 psychologists. Active clergy outnumber psychologists 17 to one, and psychiatrists 35 to one. However, only some clergymen deal some of the time with persons who are mentally or emotionally disturbed, while most psychiatrists devote their full professional attention to such persons. (Not all psychologists deal clinically with mentally ill or emotionally distressed persons; many are engaged in research, teaching, or other pursuits.)

Sheer quantity rarely tells us much about the quality of resources. Ten men with sensitivity and insight may well do more creative work in any profession than a hundred men lacking these attributes. In matters of mental health, insight must be considered not merely a tool that a pastor uses but a context within which he works.

Do theological students become "sensitized" to the nuances of human behavior, conscious and unconscious? This is a question difficult to answer. But, with more prospects of finding answers, we might ask: Are there aspects of theological education that may be singled out as resources of the churches for mental health?

Over 300 theological seminaries prepare men to serve in our 309,000 churches and synagogues. Another 400 or more prepare for other aspects of the religious life. In 1957, 83 of the former schools were Roman Catholic, 212 Protestant, eight Jewish, two Russian Orthodox, and one Greek Orthodox.

Of the 212 Protestant seminaries, 80, including six in Canada, were accredited by the American Association of Theological Schools. Forty-three, including seven in Canada and one in Puerto Rico, were associates of the A.A.T.S. Twenty-four were graduate departments of universities.

In 1959 there were 94 Roman Catholic diocesan seminaries preparing priests for service in parishes and, in addition, 424 religious or scholasticate seminaries, preparing for religious orders, teaching, and the like. (These figures are found in the official *Catholic Directory* (1959); we do not have comparable Protestant and Jewish statistics for the later year.) By including all seminaries preparing for the religious orders in addition to the pastorate, we can find a total today of over 700 theological schools for the ministries of all faiths.

There are many indescribable and unquantifiable ways in which the kind of insight is acquired that enables an individual to be a resource in matters of mental health. Some of them are factors of personality; others have to do with training and experience.

When we try to discern specific ways in which the students in our many theological schools acquire these insights and skills, we tend to focus exclusively upon courses in psychology, personality, counseling, and clinical training, and risk missing many subtle values and nuances in their theological education as a whole. Yet our focus in this chapter will be principally on what has now become known as clinical pastoral education, not because theological education as a whole is unimportant to the clergy's competence in dealing with mental health matters, but because clinical pastoral education seems to be most relevant. Further, it has become a focal point in the conversation—sometimes rather warm—between the proponents of the so-called theoretical or content studies, such as theology and church history, and the advocates of the so-called "practical" field, which includes psychology and clinical training.

The clinical pastoral education movement in theological education is one that has gone on primarily within Protestantism. Hence, with a few exceptions, what we have to say in the early portions of this chapter, particularly those parts dealing with the history of the movement, is primarily within a Protestant context. Later we will describe significant Roman Catholic and Jewish programs.

CLINICAL PASTORAL EDUCATION—AN HISTORICAL SKETCH

Paul Tillich has said that the formulation of a Christian doctrine of man is impossible today without using the material brought forth by depth psychology. Increasingly, both theologians and social scientists have recognized this need to relate religion and psychology, particularly in the training of the future clergyman.

Clinical pastoral training, or, to use the term now preferred, clinical pastoral education, was defined by the 1953 National Conference on Clinical Pastoral Training as "an opportunity for a theological student or pastor to learn pastoral care through interpersonal relations at an appropriate center such as a hospital, correctional institution, or other clinical situation, where an integrated program of theory and practice is individually supervised by a qualified chaplain supervisor, with the collaboration of an interprofessional staff."

In ancient Christian writings, a theologian is often defined as one who *first lives the Gospel* and then teaches it. Today it is again being reaffirmed that theology should be relevant to life. It is not experience alone which counts in a clinical pastoral training program, but experience together with "thinking about that experience."

In the early centuries of the Church, pastoral study, counseling, and healing were widely practiced. Lay monks often assumed pastoral counseling duties, and became known as "healers of the soul." They, in turn, were guided by the pastoral epistles of their abbots and bishops, who also communicated often with the pastors of individual churches. The pastoral letters from many bishops and elders, including those preserved in the New Testament, such as those of Paul to Timothy and Titus, constituted a kind of "clinical supervision" in the early church's equivalent of pastoral training. Pastors received many instructions, such as the following from the Persian, Aphrahat, who was a convert to Christianity:

O ye pastors, be ye made like unto that diligent Pastor, the chief of the whole flock, who cared so greatly for his flock. He brought nigh those that were afar off. He brought back the wanderers. He visited the sick. He strengthened the weak. He bound up the broken. . . . He gave himself up for the sake of the sheep." (Roberts, A., and Donaldson, J., eds., *Nicene and Post-Nicene Fathers*, 1956.)

In the *Apostolic Constitutions* bishops are enjoined to be always

. . . strengthening the weak, that is, confirming with exhortation that which is tempted; healing that which is sick, that is, curing by instruction that which is weak in the faith through doubtfulness of mind; binding up that which is broken, that is, binding up by comfortable admonitions that which is gone astray, or wounded, bruised, or broken by their sins . . . easing it of its offences, and giving hope. . . . Seek for that which is lost, that is, do not suffer that which desponds of its salvation, by reason of the multitude of its offences, utterly to perish. Do thou search for that which is grown sleepy, drowsy, and sluggish, and that which is unmindful of its own life, through the depth of its sleep, and which is at a great distance from its own flock, so as to be in danger of falling among the wolves, and being devoured by them. (Roberts and Donaldson, eds., *The Ante-Nicene Fathers,* 1951.)

The early church placed strong emphasis on gathering the known sciences together in the light of Christian faith. Minucius Felix wrote:

Man ought to know himself, and to look around and see what he is, whence he is, why he is, whether collected together from the elements, or harmoniously formed of atoms, or rather made, formed, and animated by God. And it is this very thing which we cannot seek out and investigate without inquiry into the universe, since things are so coherent, so linked and associated together, that unless you diligently examine the nature of divinity, you must be ignorant of that of humanity. Nor can you well perform your social duty unless you know that community of the world which is common to all. (Roberts and Donaldson, 1951.)

Gregory the Great, citing the superior judgment of physicians in certain healing methods, wrote of pastors: "Let them learn, therefore, let priests in their office learn, those namely to whom the cure of souls is entrusted, to observe what men of various arts under the teaching of reason attend to. . . ." (Roberts and Donaldson, 1956.)

In the ancient and medieval periods of the Church, the parish pastor was encouraged and guided in the course of a "clinical pastoral" experience by a wise "supervisor," his bishop, or an older pastor. He was also encouraged, in his preparation and in his service, to examine the nature of both divinity and humanity, to seek a relationship between theological and other disciplines, to relate his theological inquiry to "what men of various arts . . . attend to." In both aspects we see a presage of contemporary clinical pastoral education. In some ways the twentieth century development of clinical pastoral education is a continuation, a renewal, and a modification of these ancient practices.

Modern clinical pastoral education, as carried out by the Protestant churches, did not begin until the 1920's. The first regular program for seminarians in this field was started by Dr. William S. Keller, a physician and lay member of the Episcopal Church, who arranged for students of Bexley Hall Episcopal Seminary to work in public welfare and other agencies, as well as mental institutions, in Cincinnati. The program, called the Cincinnati Summer School in Social Work for Theological Students and Junior Clergy, began in 1923 with four students. As the program expanded, it drew seminarians from other denominations. Ten years later, a full-year course was introduced for graduate students. The program was officially entitled the Graduate School of Applied Religion, and in 1936 was incorporated as a nondenominational institution.

From the first, the school tried to provide clinical experiences which would equip students most practically for pastoral service. In 1944, the school became associated with the Episcopal Theological School in Cambridge, Massachusetts, while retaining the same courses and its nondenominational policy.

In 1924, Anton T. Boisen took four students for summer work under his supervision at the Worcester State Hospital in Massachusetts. This was the beginning of clinical training for mental hospital chaplains. It was then that the hospital's director, William A. Bryan, upon being questioned about the acceptance of theological students into his institution, retorted with the now legendary response that he would gladly open his doors to a horse doctor if he thought it would benefit the patients.

Anton Boisen had realized the need for clinically trained chaplains in mental institutions after his own hospitalization in the Westboro State Hospital. He was the first clinically trained chaplain in any mental hospital, and is considered by many to be the pioneer of clinical training in theological education. Now in his eighty's and officially retired, he is still active in the chaplaincy and in mental health work on a national scale.

In a personal letter to us, Dr. Boisen (1959) tells how he became concerned with a clinically trained chaplaincy for mental hospitals, and how he introduced others to the new field:

I got started in my work with the mentally ill through being a patient myself. I had a psychosis so severe that I could not fail to recognize it for what it was. At the same time it was for me a problem-solving religious experience.

It followed a crucial decision. The Interchurch World Movement, for which I had been working after my return from two years overseas with the Expeditionary Forces, had folded up. I had had a tempting offer from the Congregational Social Service Commission, but I had turned it down, because I wanted to deal more directly with living religious experience rather than with the gathering of facts and figures. I decided therefore that I would take a church. But openings were slow in coming.

While waiting I undertook to write out a statement of religious experience and a statement of belief. This was something which had been required of us at the time I came up for ordination nine years before. Since in a very real sense I was presenting myself anew, this seemed to me appropriate. I got intensely absorbed in this, so much so that I lay awake at night letting ideas take shape of themselves. This was for me nothing unusual, but this time the absorption went beyond the ordinary and ideas came surging in that simply carried me away. There were ideas of coming world disaster, of my own unsuspected importance, and the like.

I stood it for several days. Then the pressure became so great that I began to share my fears with my people. Of course they became afraid also, but afraid of me, and very soon I found myself in the Boston Psychopathic Hospital and shortly thereafter in the Westboro State Hospital. All the while I was violently excited.

In those days hydrotherapy was the chief reliance, but the turning point came with a discovery which I made myself. At Westboro I was placed on the sleeping porch. There I noticed that the Moon was centered on a cross of light. This alarmed me greatly. For what did the cross mean? It stood for suffering, and the Moon, which I thought of as a living being, is grieving over the situation. In order to be sure I checked with one of the attendants and my fears were confirmed. He also saw the cross. For several days my terror continued. Then I made another discovery. Whenever I looked at the Moon from a certain spot, the cross did not appear. Investigation showed that from this particular spot I was looking at the Moon through a hole in the wire screening. With this discovery the delusional edifice which I was building up was swept away, and in a few days I was moved to a better ward.

My first reaction was that of tremendous curiosity about what had happened to me. I was sure that I was physically sound before the disturbance and certainly I was in good shape afterwards. I tried to recall everything I could of my experience and I wrote lengthy letters recording the memories and giving my interpretation of them. I also observed other patients on my ward, and more and more I was convinced that the trouble in most of my fellow patients was a religious one. But there was no recognition of that fact.

I wanted to talk over my problems with my doctor, but I found him unresponsive. I went to the chapel services on Sunday afternoon but I felt that the ministers knew little about our problems. And all the time I was trying desperately to convince my friends that I was as well as I had ever been, only to find that the harder I tried the less they were convinced. The result was an accentuation of my own fears and of a sense of helplessness, and after four and a half months there came a second disturbance. Again this came on suddenly. It was also extremely severe and it lasted ten weeks. And again I awakened as out of a bad dream.

Though much discouraged at this set-back, I felt that I was now on the way to finding the solution to my vocational problem. I began by looking around on the convalescent ward where I was. I found that thirteen of the twenty-five men were on the ward all day long with nothing to do but think. I wrote a memorandum to my doctor calling his attention to the situation and offering some suggestions. I wrote a second memorandum suggesting some work assignments, including wood-working and photography. A third memorandum outlined a plan for a play festival for July Fourth. And I didn't say a word about getting out. The doctors were interested.

I was commissioned to proceed with the July Fourth plans and I was given the photographic assignment. In about six weeks I was told I was ready for discharge, but my people had been so thoroughly frightened by the severity of the disturbance and so discouraged by the set-back that actually it took seven months. But I made good use of the time. I made a survey of the hospital in pictures and I staged other play festivals.

Fifteen months in the Westboro State Hospital was then my first step. I have Bishop Norman Nash to thank for my next step. He helped me get an absolute discharge from the hospital and then to enter the Graduate School of Harvard University. There, under Richard Cabot, Macfie Campbell and William McDougall, I sought to acquaint myself with what was known about mental illness and its relationship to religious experience. With increasing knowledge I became more and more convinced that the theories I had worked out by myself were essentially correct and that mental illness was indeed a problem which concerned the minister of religion as much as it did the medical man.

As I saw it then, and still see it, the major problems of non-organic mental illness have to do with the sense of "guilt," or "sin," with "cure" or "salvation," with "voices," or "inspirations," and the like. The problems are much the same, though the vocabulary and approach are different. By this I mean that the religionist was making little use of the methods of science in his attempt to explore and understand human nature; while the psychiatrist, and likewise the psychologist, the sociologist, and the anthropologist, who made use of scientific methodology, were very seldom carrying their inquiries over to the level of the religious. The field of religious experience and its relationship to mental illness remained then a no-man's land, almost entirely unexplored.

I stayed at Harvard two and a half years, much longer than I had planned. Already at the end of the first semester I was looking for some way of applying my new insights. My first thought was of a chaplaincy in some mental hospital. But the doors did not open. Most of the state hospitals, where 90 per cent of our mental patients are housed, have religious services, but they were then little more than a gesture. Any suggestion that a minister of religion might have something to contribute and much to learn in the mental hospital was coldly received.

But the next winter Dr. Bryan of the Worcester State Hospital expressed a willingness to try out a chaplain. Here was the opening for which I was looking.

So far as I am aware, I entered upon my duties at Worcester as the first mental hospital chaplain with any special training. I went there with the clear understanding that I was to serve as chaplain and research worker (the latter under the auspices of the Chicago Theological Seminary). I was to have no responsibility for such things as recreational activities, library, or post office and I was to have free access to the case records, the right to visit all the wards, and to attend the staff meetings at which the cases were discussed.

A few months after my arrival at Worcester I made visits to several theological schools to see if there might not be students who would be interested in working as attendants and chaplain-trainees, in order to learn something about the problem of mental illness. In the summer of 1925 we had four such students. That was the beginning of the clinical training plan, so far as I was concerned in it. In 1928 there were eleven students. To-day there are some 50 training centers, and over 6,000 persons have taken advantage of the opportunities thus offered. The clinical training plan has now been extended to include general hospitals and penal institutions.

While there is reason for gratification in the growth of the movement, its original objectives are still far from being achieved. The No-Man's Land between the religious and the medical workers is still unexplored. We are still accepting psychiatric dogma on authority. This had been right and necessary. We are still learners and medical men have much to teach us. But there are significant questions which we must ask and it is essential that we formulate those questions and develop methods of answering them which will stand up under criticism. The movement as a whole must be undergirded by a program of inquiry.

Dr. Boisen has often stated that he had not been trying to introduce anything new to the theological curriculum, but had been trying to focus attention again on the central problem of theology and the central task of the church—the problem of sin and salvation. It is not the content but the approach which is new; we study not from textbooks, he has affirmed, but from living human documents.

In the 1930's Dr. Boisen became chaplain at the Elgin State Hospital in Illinois, where he continued his training programs with the Chicago Theological Seminary. The movement started by him in Worcester, incorporated in 1930 as the Council for Clinical Training, continued to emphasize work with the mentally ill, though it expanded its program to include general hospitals in 1932, correctional institutions in 1936, and institutions for juvenile offenders in 1940. At first the Council worked with almost no assistance from the seminaries, sometimes in the face of opposition from them.

The Institute of Pastoral Care, which began in the early 1930's and was known simply as the "New England Group," was from its beginning closely allied with four theological seminaries: the Episcopal Theological School, Andover Newton, Boston University School of Theology, and Harvard Divinity School. The Episcopal Theological School since 1937 has made clinical training a requirement for graduation. In contrast to the Council, the Institute centered its work in general hospitals. The founders of this movement, and the first to bring clinical training into a general hospital, were Dr. Richard C. Cabot, a surgeon and professor in the Harvard Medical School; Russell L. Dicks, chaplain of the Massachusetts General Hospital, and Dr. Austin Philip Guiles, who in 1931 was appointed director of Clinical Pastoral Training at Andover Newton Theological School.

The New England Group aimed at bringing clinical training under the control of theological schools in preference to promotion by an incorporated or private group. With this aim, faculty members from Andover Newton, Episcopal Theological School, and Harvard Divinity School, in 1938, organized the Theological Schools' Committee on Clinical Training to sponsor and direct the summer courses in clinical training offered at the Massachusetts General Hospital, Boston City Hospital, and the State Infirmary at Tewksbury. This committee finally became what is known as the Institute of Pastoral Care.

The first theological school to make a full clinical training program obligatory for all students was the Divinity School of the Protestant Episcopal Church in Philadelphia. From 1937 students were required to spend the first quarter of each academic year in clinical training at Philadelphia State Hospital, in cooperation with the Council for Clinical Training.

After four years, a three-term year was adopted, the first twelve weeks being given to clinical training, preceding the academic course. This change, according to Dr. Reuel L. Howe (1945), first director of the program, provided the student an opportunity "to evaluate himself and his resources, educational, interpretive, and personal, before he began his theological studies. It was found, for instance, that nearly all of the students needed to re-evaluate their experiences, and the theology that they had brought with them. . . . The familiarity with and understanding of people and human problems acquired during the first training period enabled them to begin their study of theological subjects with a greater sense of reality."

A major stimulus to the development of clinical pastoral training programs was the Second World War. Many servicemen tended to regard religion as abstract, formal, and impractical because, as Chaplain Charles Carpenter (1945) expressed it, "so often the sermonizing of the civilian preachers had been based upon careful study and wide reading, but carried with it little of the reality and knowledge of the problems that were personal and intimate to individuals." Military chaplains sometimes found it difficult to help servicemen who had had this kind of church experience at home to see religion as a worthwhile factor in their lives.

The unpreparedness of many chaplains was particularly distressing to themselves as well as to others. With little experience in personal counseling, they found it difficult to attempt such counseling now with the troops. Too often they tried to give direction, rather than to listen sympathetically.

When the war began, there were only 138 regular Army chaplains.

The many who served later were volunteers from their home parishes. The Army was forced to start rapid training schedules in service counseling, which owed much to the work of Carl Rogers and his client-centered method of initial counseling. Rogers spent a year traveling to Army camps in connection with these programs.

After the war, the returning servicemen and women presented a new challenge to religious leaders at home. Much counseling was needed to help veterans to adapt to college life, to business, or to their families. There was a great demand for education, vocational guidance, and counseling psychologists. Projects were begun to assist veterans in their readjustment to civilian life. Many returning veterans had come to expect closer relationships with their priests, ministers, or rabbis, competent personal counseling for themselves and others, and sermons that deal knowledgeably with human problems. In several ways, then, the war experience gave impetus to the clinical pastoral training movement—among them being the servicemen's experience of a ministry highly relevant to their needs in a situation of alternating danger and boredom, and the development of new procedures in secular counseling.

The individuals whose work we have described, and many others as well, have constantly sought greater cooperation among seminaries and agencies in pastoral training. The first National Conference on Clinical Training in Theological Education, for example, was sponsored by the Council for Clinical Training, the Graduate School of Applied Religion, and the Institute of Pastoral Care, with representatives of theological schools. The first publication devoted exclusively to this field, *The Journal of Pastoral Care,* was published jointly by the Council and the Institute. National committees have set standards for clinical pastoral education. Now a permanent national group, the Advisory Committee on Clinical Pastoral Education, has been formed from five sponsoring groups: The Association of Seminary Professors in the Practical Fields, the Council for Clinical Training, the Institute of Pastoral Care, the Lutheran Advisory Council, and the Southern Baptist Association for Clinical Pastoral Education.

PROGRAMS IN CLINICAL PASTORAL EDUCATION

In the remainder of this chapter we discuss several ways in which theological students—and clergymen in the parish—are provided with opportunities for gaining understanding of personality dynamics and related subjects, particularly through supervised clinical experience.

Some, though not all, of our emphasis is on what is now commonly called clinical pastoral education. We know of only two attempts to assess any of these programs, and these are subjective rather than objective; hence our remarks are descriptive rather than evaluative.

Under the Council for Clinical Training and the Institute of Pastoral Care the clinical resources for pastoral training of Protestant theological students have increased in recent years. The Lutheran Advisory Council and the Southern Baptist Association for Clinical Pastoral Education have also sponsored the expansion of this training.

The 212 Protestant seminaries in the United States now have a total of 343 programs in clinical pastoral training, counseling, or psychology, ranging from short-term lecture and seminar courses to intensive clinical training. A compilation by the Department of Pastoral Services of the National Council of Churches (1958), published in the annual directory issue of *Pastoral Psychology* for January, 1958, divides the 343 programs into five groups according to the type and intensity of the training.

In the first group are short-term programs consisting of lecture series, conferences, and seminars on pastoral care and counseling. These are offered by 16 seminaries, 26 councils of churches, and 15 universities and other institutions. Group two consists of 105 seminaries offering seminary courses on pastoral care and psychology, with orientation and observation courses in clinical pastoral training, with some field trips to institutions. These are primarily lecture and reading courses with some practical demonstrations or supervised field work.

Group three includes seminary and university programs which

offer clinical observation or supervision of clinical experience in general or mental hospitals, correctional institutions, or other agencies. They are usually at an introductory level. Seventy-one theological schools and two other institutions are listed.

In the fourth group are 21 institutions offering comprehensive courses in pastoral care which lead to the Master's or Doctor's degree in pastoral theology, pastoral counseling, and clinical psychology, with related theological courses. In group five are 87 organizations offering at least six weeks supervised resident and full-time training in an accredited center or agency. Only the last three types of program give the student first-hand relationships with patients.

The Council for Clinical Training lists 11 general hospitals, 25 mental hospitals, 7 correctional institutions, and 6 specialized agencies as centers for training under its auspices. The council is an interdenominational, non-sectarian, non-profit corporation, organized to provide qualified supervision of theological students working with people under stress.

Under the Institute of Pastoral Care are 18 general hospitals, 26 mental hospitals, and 4 correctional institutions. The Institute, a nonsectarian educational foundation, offers courses lasting either six or twelve weeks. In each hospital or other training center, accredited chaplain-supervisors are in charge of instruction, assisted by qualified associates, in a ratio of one supervisor to each five or six students. Both theological students and clergymen are accepted for training. The National Lutheran Council has approved 15 institutions for chaplaincy training.

Of the hundred programs in which theological students, as well as ordained clergymen, receive supervised clinical experience, we will describe here a dozen or so, selected to illustrate current trends in clinical pastoral education. We would also call attention to other significant programs, which will not be treated in detail here, such as that conducted by Boston University School of Theology under the direction of Dr. Paul E. Johnson at one general hospital (Massachusetts Memorial), two psychiatric hospitals (Massachusetts Mental Health Center and Boston State Hospital) and in the Boston University School of Theology Counseling Service; the program at Elgin State Hospital, Elgin, Illinois, formerly directed by Anton Boisen and presently by Clarence Bruninga; at Central State Griffin Memorial Hospital, Norman, Oklahoma, conducted by Mack Powell and with five seminaries participating; at Pacific School of Religion, Berkeley, California, directed by Robert Leslie; the clinical program of the American Foundation of Religion and Psychiatry (discussed in Chapter 5); the School of Pastoral Care conducted by Richard K. Young at North Carolina Baptist Hospital at Winston-Salem and Southeastern Baptist Theological Seminary.

The application of the principles of clinical pastoral education to the general rather than the mental hospital was particularly the contribution of Russell Dicks, Richard Cabot, and Philip Guiles. In most clinical programs in the general hospital setting seminarians in training deal only peripherally with patients who are mentally ill and directly with those who are under stress of various kinds— physical pain, anxiety, guilt, and the like. Thus the general hospital setting may be more analogous to the situation with which the pastor will later have to deal in the parish.

The Clinical Training Program at Boston City Hospital, started in the early 1930's by Dr. Austin Philip Guiles, was the first in a general hospital and is now the largest single hospital program for theological students. Sponsored by Andover Newton Theological School and the Institute of Pastoral Care, it is one of the 18 programs in general hospitals under the supervision of the Institute. Nearly all Protestant denominations and the Eastern Orthodox Church have been represented among the students. Training centers at Massachusetts Memorial Hospital and Worcester State Hospital are now carrying related aspects of the program. The training is supervised by Dr. John M. Billinsky, Guiles Professor of Psychology and Clinical Training at Andover Newton, and Andrew D. Elia, M.D., physician and visiting professor at Andover Newton. Harvard, Boston University, and Tufts University medical schools provide faculty members.

The summer program is an intensive twelve-week course under sixteen specialists; about seventy students are usually enrolled, spending the first two weeks as orderlies, and the remainder visiting patients and participating in seminars and lectures. Each student is encouraged to see at least one patient consistently so that the development of the student-patient relationship may be fully observed.

Besides the summer program, B.D. and S.T.M. candidates are in training throughout the year. Although this training program has provided a large number of hospital and armed forces chaplains, its primary focus is on the clinical training of clergymen for parish work. A 1956 report shows that of 1148 students who had completed one or more summer sessions since their inauguration in 1931, 132 were serving as chaplains in armed forces, 23 as chaplains in Veterans Administration hospitals, 72 as chaplains in general hospitals, 39 as chaplains in mental hospitals, 6 as chaplains in colleges, 17 as professors in theological schools, and 745 as pastors of parishes.

Clinical pastoral training for Protestant seminarians at St. Elizabeths Hospital, operated under government auspices in Washington, D.C., began in 1945. Most students in this mental hospital program are preparing for the parish ministry rather than the chaplaincy. (Special intensive courses for the latter are described in Chapter 1.) A full-time, twelve-week program is offered to students at least once a year, usually in the summer. Advanced students are in training during the full year.

The course is open to students holding a college degree who have completed a year in a theological seminary, to graduate students, and to ordained clergymen. About twelve Protestant denominations have been represented in most sessions; Roman Catholic priests from the Catholic University program, referred to below, have participated in the psychiatric part of the program while remaining under the supervision of their own chaplain.

The Protestant chaplain, Ernest E. Bruder, describes the goals and content of clinical pastoral training at St. Elizabeths as follows (Bruder and Barb, 1956):

Our objectives are to help the student become acquainted with the mentally ill patient; to learn something about mental illness—its theory, problems, and management; and to evaluate the relationship between religion and psychiatry and the pastor's role in relation to the mentally ill. . . .

The course includes extensive interviewing of patients, participating and preaching in the worship activities of the hospital, attendance at general staff conferences, observation of therapies, participating in some training activities of the psychiatric residents, at least one private conference with the Chaplain Supervisor each week, lectures from staff physicians on the dynamics of mental illness, lectures from staff chaplains on specific aspects of the mental hospital chaplaincy.

The Clinical Pastoral Education movement is primarily a Protestant phenomenon. Among the more than 500 Roman Catholic seminaries (94 of these are diocesan seminaries preparing for the parish), few courses or programs are offered in supervised clinical training, although many academic courses are given in psychology and related fields. Courses in psychology and psychiatry in Catholic universities are also available for seminarians and clergy. Apart from these, the Roman Catholic Church has seven centers specifically for training chaplains and priests who want more extensive clinical experience. One of these is the program conducted by the Catholic University of America in Washington, D.C., and centered in St. Elizabeths Hospital. Most of the students in this program have already been ordained to the priesthood and are specifically interested in the mental hospital chaplaincy.

Students in training may work either for a Certificate in Chaplain Training or for a Master's degree, together with this Certificate. In the latter case, they must meet all departmental and Graduate School requirements for the M.A. degree.

The Catholic University program is directed by the Rev. John W. Stafford, C.S.V., head of the Department of Psychology at Catholic University, and the Rev. Wilbur F. Wheeler. Casework is conducted at the university; supervised training at St. Elizabeths Hospital and other centers. The Veterans' Administration, which influenced the launching of the program, still lends support; financial aid also comes from the Department of Health, Education, and Welfare.

Among the Roman Catholic staff and students a tendency to

separate spiritual and psychological matters can be discerned. At the Catholic University counseling center, for example, persons who come for help are referred to different counselors, depending on whether they want to discuss a moral or a psychological problem. A further difference is found in the intention on the part of the Protestant staff to provide this specialized training as a prelude to work in the parish. The Roman Catholic view is that at this early stage many pre-ordination students are not mature enough to deal with some of the problems raised during the course of clinical experience. Furthermore, it is not practical to train a man highly and then lose him in a small community parish. "We must be realistic," says Father Stafford, "and agree that in this generation, at least, we must try to place these competent people in administrative and teaching positions so that their influence will 'filter down.'" All the priests who have received higher degrees or certificates in this program have been assigned to seminaries, hospitals, and counseling centers.

For students preparing for the rabbinate at the three major Jewish theological schools the only clinical program is that of the Institute for Pastoral Psychiatry of the New York Board of Rabbis. Bellevue Hospital in New York City and Jacobi Hospital, associated with the Albert Einstein School of Medicine, are used as training centers for Yeshiva University, the Jewish Theological Seminary of America, and Hebrew Union College-Jewish Institute of Religion.

All three major Jewish seminaries in New York City use the Institute's training program, under the direction of Rabbi I. Fred Hollander. The program is not limited to chaplaincy candidates, since few mental hospitals have enough Jewish patients to warrant full-time chaplains. Rabbi Hollander is "seeking to demarcate an area of functioning which would be harmonious with the role of the clergyman, not only the rabbi but also the Protestant and Catholic pastor as well." His interest is in "the kind of orientation relevant to the function of the clergy . . . and a program of training which will be relevant to the clergyman's role." We will refer later in more detail to the program at Yeshiva University.

Two traditions underlie the new programs in clinical pastoral education at Union Theological Seminary in New York City. One is the work of the late David A. Roberts, who gave the first courses at Union in theology and psychiatry. The other is the requirement on the part of all degree candidates for a prescribed term of field work in parish or institutional setting.

The current threefold program—for the Bachelor of Divinity degree, for the Master of Sacred Theology and for the Doctor of Theology in the field of Practical Theology—began in the fall of 1956 with Earl A. Loomis, Jr., M.D. as director, Dr. Charles R. Stinnette, Jr., as associate director, and Dr. Jack C. Greenwalt as counseling director.

Theological students receive supervised training at St. Luke's Hospital, the Presbyterian Hospital, Englewood County Hospital (New Jersey), and Rikers Island Prison. The Union program is unusual in running throughout the year, and not only in the summer. Students must spend seven and a half hours a week in actual clinical training throughout the year under supervision.

The goal of the program is not to prepare theological students to become counselors; rather, its main purpose is "the strengthening of the training of prospective ministers for their tasks in introducing them to the understanding of human behavior afforded by contemporary psychodynamics." The courses and clinical experience are meant to provide psychiatric insight "wherever that insight is relevant in the training of religious workers and teachers."

Dr. Loomis (1957) believes it is especially important that

the candidate's personality should further the achievement of legitimate aims in the Christian ministry and that problems in personality which stand in the way of achieving those aims should be solved. Ways of evaluating personal adequacy and growth will have to be developed. Much will be learned regarding the candidate's own personality situation through his experience in being supervised and in supervising. Beyond this, in each case that seems to require it, it will be recommended that a candidate for the degree should have enough sessions in counseling or in psychotherapy to assist in the removal of barriers which might otherwise stand in the way of his effectiveness in the very type of work in which he is specializing.

The program in clinical pastoral training at the Institute of Religion at the Texas Medical Center in Houston was initiated by the medical profession itself, when the Administrative Council of the Center requested the Council of Churches of Greater Houston to study the possibility of religious activities within the Center. Subsequently, the Medical Center asked that an Institute of Religion be started there to give courses to both theological and medical students and to be linked with the five theological seminaries in Texas, with Baylor University College of Medicine, and with the nursing schools of the associated hospitals. The Institute now has access to the Methodist Hospital, Baylor University College of Medicine, the M. D. Anderson Cancer and Tumor Research Hospital, four general hospitals, two children's hospitals, the Memorial Baptist Hospital, and the Veterans' Administration Hospitals.

Seminary students and pastors are offered training in order to become familiar with procedures in medical institutions and problems of individuals in stress. Reciprocally, Baylor University College of Medicine, through the Institute of Religion, offers elective courses in religion and medicine to medical students, nursing students, and doctors, so that they can learn of the resources that the church can offer them in their practice.

The Institute of Religion, under the direction of Dr. Dawson C. Bryan, provides three programs for degree candidates. The first is a three months' summer course for students who have a minimum of two years' theological training. All five seminaries that participate in the program give credit toward the B.D. degree for this course. The second is an internship in pastoral care for ministers who are working toward the Master's degree in theology. Such a student would be allowed to complete his degree only after returning to one of the five participating schools for additional courses, the Institute's chief concern being, in the words of Dr. Bryan (1957), that the student "through pastoral clinical direction is related to his total seminary education in such fashion that biblically, doctrinally, organizationally his *pastoral* ministry is a unity." The third course is a second year of residency, for those expecting to work for a doctoral degree. The Institute also conducts seminars, workshops, and training courses for clergymen from Houston and other communities in the state.

A symbol of the search for greater interplay between religion and psychiatry and of the growing interest in their interrelationship in dealing with the "whole patient" is the joint chair in religion and medicine at the University of Chicago, occupied by the Rev. Granger E. Westberg. A former hospital chaplain, Mr. Westberg conducts courses in religion for medical students and clinical training for theological students. An example of the scope of the courses is that given for second year medical students. Among the topics discussed are the role of the family in illness, grief reactions, interrelationship of religion and psychiatry, religious aspects of functional illnesses, premarital counseling, birth control. For theological students clinical training programs are arranged in such a way that the students split the day between seminary and hospital. A unique aspect of the program is that in which both theological and medical students take part: frequent conferences at which a student chaplain or a medical intern discusses the religious and clinical implications of a patient's history.

In *The Advancement of Theological Education* (1957), the authors (H. Richard Niebuhr, Daniel Day Williams, and James M. Gustafson, p. 123) extend the term "clinical training" from the customary hospital setting to include nearly any learning situation "in which the conditions of technical supervision and controlled observation are present." In such a situation "the theological student can be led to a deeper understanding of his ministry and can acquire skill in dealing with human problems" by encountering and dealing with "specific human needs with the help of supervisors who bring experience and technical knowledge to bear upon the kinds of problems under consideration."

The program at Yale Divinity School embodies this wider, delimited interpretation of "clinical" experience, while providing a substantial and broad framework of psychology closely related to theology. The basic insights of psychology, says James E. Dittes, Assistant Professor of Psychology, should be of just as much importance in enriching the study of theology, ethics, Bible, and church history, as in the more practical fields of religious education and the pastorate. In a personal communication prepared especially for this report, Dr. Dittes (1959) states:

One's sense of the relation between pastoral theology and psychology is strengthened by the fact that pastroal theology seems to be the point at which all of the various fragments of the theological curriculum need to be integrated. It is in the experience of stepping, himself, into the role of pastor that the student can most profitably bring to bear on a common target the various elements of his theological training.

This process of integration and fructification itself is a psychological, not merely an intellectual, process which must go on within the person—or more accurately, within the person in his vocational role. This necessarily requires considerable attention to the personality of the student or pastor himself and to how he *feels* the theological truth and the needs of his parishioners and the resources of religious institutions.

For example, in confronting a situation of bereavement, the new pastor has available to him the formal rituals of the church, certain theological notions concerning death and resurrection, a psychological understanding of grief, and perhaps other fragments he has picked up in various parts of his curriculum. He also has an important element, his own attitudes and feelings about death, and he has his own experiences in this connection. The most typical reaction of the young pastor is to emphasize one or another of these resources. . . . Ideally, all these things can be related into a rich "package" of pastoral care. But such relationship is difficult and is largely a personal psychological job. It might be achieved through a clinical course which would allow a student to be exposed to various situations of stress requiring pastoral care and allow him to work through, in the company of a trusted counselor, his own personal sense of how to deal with such situations. Such personal consultation should be clearly distinguished from psychotherapy, though in some instances there may be personal handicaps towards effective pastoral care which require therapy. The goal should be called something like "effective vocational functioning," rather than "mental health" or "effective personal functioning."

The insistence on the autonomy of psychology as a separate area of the curriculum focuses on the importance of a clear foundation in psychology. The required introductory course, Psychological Foundations of Personality, attempts in one semester to introduce students to the basic concepts and types of analysis current in the understanding of personality, particularly motivational and dynamic aspects of personality. This course is intended to be of help to students in developing their theological views and also in developing their various pastoral activities; it has no particular orientation simply towards personal counseling. In this respect it varies from the basic courses offered in other theological seminaries.

From the basic course in personality, students can go either into courses in counseling or in Psychology of Religion. Each of these courses is aimed toward providing analytical tools and understanding of psychological principles which can be of general use in any application. The work in counseling is given because students think that is what they want. The counseling course is in actuality an advanced course in personality which explores particular concepts of man and analyzes certain human plights. Such study should be helpful toward developing theological understanding and toward enlightening all pastoral activities, not just counseling. The work in the Psychology of Religion also is chiefly an advanced course in personality, with some social psychology thrown in. In the field of the psychology of religion, the only fruitful strategy is to begin to make an explicit use of concepts and analytical tools developed in other areas of psychology. Therefore, such concepts are introduced from personality and social psychology, which seem to offer the most possible illumination of religious behavior and experience. Again, the full range of possible application is assumed.

The final course in the sequence is a research seminar in which, as the catalogue says, "students undertake research projects relating psychological knowledge to another field of inquiry or to problems of a vocational field, or they will undertake empirical research dealing with psychological variables relevant to religious inquiry."

The view that the entire curriculum should be oriented toward pastoral theology influences the way in which all of these courses are handled. None of this is intended to be study of man in abstract, but rather everything is focused towards helping the student better understand himself in a pastoral relationship with others. The types of concepts and analytical tools chosen to present to students and the illustrations and examples which are employed are all so intended. In the advanced course in personal counseling this is carried out most explicitly. In this course, limited to eight students, the students are given clinical experience in calling as pastors on individuals and then afforded close personal supervision (an hour of consultation for each hour of pastoral visit) in which, it is hoped, the important learning experiences take place. These experiences are those of trying to integrate his various concepts and opinions and personal feelings into his vocational role.

Sometimes the individual consultations deal with theological problems, sometimes with psychological concepts, often with the student's own feelings and fears. In each instance, the material is that which is evoked by the immediate pastoral experience; and presumably the development of theological, psychological, and self-understanding in the context and under the impact of such an experience serves to personalize it and make it more effectively available than otherwise would be the case. This year the students have had pastoral experiences in the Community Hospital and in one of the local schools where they have consulted with children on referral from the school's social worker and guidance counselor.

The almost faddish popularity of pastoral counseling in the last decade or two can be understood on several grounds. One, the insights of dynamic psychology have mostly emerged out of psychotherapy and are most easily applied to something resembling psychotherapy as closely as possible. This is true even though in principle such insights are applicable to any dealings with human beings. Two, ministers are made very aware of the great misery and suffering involved in personal and inter-personal problems, and they are highly motivated to take some effective remedial action. That which seems most available to them is to function as some kind of lay-psychotherapist. Third, ministers who feel substantial ambiguity in their vocational calling and in their religious commitment, as many ministers do, feel considerably more comfortable in taking some kind of effective action towards meeting human plights, by-passing the more traditional religious forms and vocabulary. There was a time when ministers could reach this personal compromise by taking part in vigorous social action. As social action fell into some disrespect, pastoral counseling seems to have come along to take its place in serving this psychological function for ministers.

There are signs that, just as social action has become better integrated into theological and ethical thought and into the institutions of the church, the basic psychological insights are now being more generally utilized in the total range of pastoral activity. Instead of engaging in personal counseling as an extra, pasted-on activity, abandoning the usual religious modes, there is a growing tendency for pastors to be equally psychological, but psychological in their traditional religious role.

Clinical training itself, of course, is only a procedure, in spite of the fact that some people become so infatuated with the procedure that they regard it as an end in itself. But this procedure has been successively pointed toward different ends. There have been times when the primary emphases seem to be on the development of counseling skills and on personal therapy for pastors. The best leaders, including Boisen, have always had the larger goal in mind, but these have become predominant only in recent years with the development of a new generation of leaders of the clinical training movement. Now the goal of clinical training seems to be fairly explicitly the general application of psychological insights to the total range of pastoral activities.

The growing conviction that some form of clinical training ought to be included in the curriculum of the theological seminary has been matched by the increasing dilemma of the faculties, who have had to find place for it in already overcrowded programs. A sample survey of 25 theological seminaries made by Niebuhr *et al.*, (1956), as one of several preliminaries to his national study of theological education points to one dilemma in which the schools find themselves:

They cannot in three years deal with *all* of the subjects that seem to be required in any good theological curriculum and at the same time give their students adequate preparation in *each* of these subjects. They face the choice of either offering a very small amount of work in all of the disciplines of an expanded theological curriculum and so short-changing the student in each one of them; or otherwise of resolutely excising from the course some essential studies so as to give adequate attention to those that remain. . . . Several tendencies in the recent development of the theological curriculum are clearly indicated. In the first place there is remarkable constancy so far as requirements in Biblical studies, Church History, Theology, and Preaching are concerned. . . . Secondly, there has been a considerable tendency to increase the number of required courses. Eight more schools now require Christian Ethics than did so in 1935; seven more require psychology; six, pastoral theology. . . . Thirdly, the most remarkable increase had been in the requirement of field work. Few schools give academic credit for this type of training; but very many add this demand on the student's time and energies to the requirements represented by the course credit system. It becomes apparent how slight the requirements are in some fields now that accommodation has been made for the addition of new subjects. . . . Very little attention indeed can be devoted to psychology in a course which demands one per cent of a student's time and effort. . . . What happens to a curriculum when significant additions are made in psychology and Christian Ethics? The answer is that older courses are all filed down a little to make room for the new.

The Niebuhr report proposes some solutions. The first is a four-year program for the Bachelor of Divinity degree—an end to the "three-year strait jacket." The chief problem here is that either schools "will need to reduce by a quarter the number of students they will graduate each year, or they must increase their facilities so that they can take care of one-third more students." A second suggestion is the improvement of pretheological education. Niebuhr says that the complaint of theological professors "is not that students come to them without a knowledge of Hebrew but without adequate ability to read and write English effectively. The general difficulty presented by entering students is not only that they are frequently unacquainted with Biblical thought but also that they have had little or no preparation in history, philosophy, sociology, and psychology." A third answer is the "vicarage," or "internship" year, following the custom of medical schools. Here the main obstacle is the inadequacy of supervision and guidance, as has been seen in programs already in effect. A fourth proposal, the Post-B.D. Summer School, has been tried with some success at some schools.

EXPERIMENTAL PROGRAMS IN RELIGION
AND MENTAL HEALTH

In 1956, three theological centers (one Roman Catholic, one Protestant, and one Jewish) were awarded grants by the National Institute of Mental Health to plan extended programs of instruction and research in religion and mental health. These pilot programs seek a curriculum which would use all the behavioral sciences in theological education: not only psychology and psychiatry but sociology, anthropology, and medicine.

The ultimate goal for the five-year period is to acquaint theological students with knowledge about mental health, to help them become more effective clergymen through greater insight into themselves and others, and particularly to develop a curriculum that could be used in other seminaries and that would reflect several disciplines and relate new learning and insights to the three major faiths.

The three schools—Loyola University in Chicago, Harvard Divinity School in Cambridge, and Yeshiva University in New York City—share their findings and evaluate their programs every three months. The Rev. George Christian Anderson, Director of the Academy of Religion and Mental Health and one of those most responsible for the inauguration of the programs, explains that these evaluations are based largely on changes of attitude or achievement among the students, and have the additional purpose of relating as much new learning as possible, during the course of the programs, to the theology of the three religious traditions.

The Loyola project in religion and mental health began with a course on "the psychodynamics of personality development." Later, additional courses on personality were added, including religious development; on small group dynamics, particularly the family; on problems of personality maladjustments; and on interviewing and guidance. The aim is "to develop in the young priest a conception of the dynamic nature of personality and of the social processes to aid him in the effective discharge of his priestly role with his parishioners."

The Loyola project, directed by the Rev. Vincent V. Herr, S.J., Ph.D., the Rev. William J. Devlin, S.J., M.D., and the Rev. Charles A. Curran, Ph.D., is already working with Roman Catholic seminaries, supplying them with educational materials and getting evaluations from their students.

Father Herr (1958) describes the three main categories of evaluation as interviewing (on tape), projective testing, and objective testing. Evaluations are made at Loyola of those currently active in the program—faculty, administrators and students, and priests active outside the group. The findings from these sources are used in the "construction of curricular materials relevant to the role of the contemporary priest." The trainee's role, according to an informal statement by the project directors, is not as a diagnostician nor as a therapist:

Through a broader knowledge of the behavioral sciences, he is the person who uses his own religious resources more positively and effectively in the salvation of souls. With such additional knowledge of the dynamic and motivational factors in man, he can aid in the preservation of mental health. He does this by encouraging proper and positive moral and religious experiences, and he will foster such experiences throughout the whole growth of the dynamically evolving personality. In this manner he will aid the parishioner in the development of a wholesome, mature personality.

To describe the second related project, we quote directly from a personal communication from Dr. Hans Hofmann, Associate Professor of Theology at Harvard Divinity School and director of the program:

The Harvard University project on religion and mental health has been set up in order to implement the present day theological curricula in this country with instruction in and investigation of the relationship between these two critical areas, religion and mental health. The goal is to prepare the prospective ministers to deal constructively with the emotional and mental problems in the lives of their parishioners, and make easy and early referrals where this is necessary. The implied concept of mental health is therefore the ability to cope constructively with one's own life problems in order to avoid mental strain or emotional instability. The community agencies, including the clergy, are seen as able to detect those people who need their help and to enlist, without hesitancy, the assistance of the psychotherapist when this is indicated.

One level on which the project works is the training of prospective ministers, in close consultation with the psychiatrist assigned to the Harvard Divinity School. The student, once admitted, is closely observed with respect to the growth of his personal development and his ability to integrate the knowledge he acquires with his understanding of his personal faith and with his function of communicating the Christian faith to others. A member of the department of theology confronts the traditional Hebraic-Christian understanding of the human personality with the insights which contemporary social sciences and psychotherapy have produced.

A clinical psychologist deals with instruction in the field of psychology of personality and abnormal psychology. Often enough the theological student receives an insufficient preparation in the field of psychology. This must be amended by sharpening the focus on those psychological insights which relate directly to understanding the human personality in its changing relation to its environment. The theoretical concepts are taught in lectures, in order to give the student knowledge of what is meant by the different psychological terms and the clinical data they describe. To illustrate the human reality represented in such abstract terms and concepts, case material is presented and then freely discussed by students and instructor.

In the setting of the Massachusetts Mental Health Center, a course is given entitled "Introduction to Psychopathology and Psychotherapy." A member of the house staff enlists, in sequence, the contributions of the psychiatrist, the social worker, the psychologist, the chaplain, and the nurses to demonstrate to the students the functioning of a mental institution. The students follow the patient's development from admission through discharge. Such a realistic appraisal of the nature and function of a mental institution is especially desirable when the minister is called upon to counsel either a prospective patient or his relatives and friends. He should be able to describe accurately the relevance of private and hospital psychotherapy and remove as radically as possible the stigma which is usually attached to psychotherapeutic treatment. He should also be able to keep in contact with the hospitalized patient and help him to assume a cooperative attitude to the ongoing treatment and his therapist. Only when the pastor is able to communicate intelligently with the house staff of the hospital is he able to function as a link between them and the patient, as well as between the relatives and the patient. Upon discharge, the minister should be able to facilitate the patient's return to his community, family, and professional situation. He will have to help overcome fears and hesitancy on both sides. An important task of the clergy is to dispel the unjustified reluctance of our society, and especially of religious groups, to readmit a former mental patient into the full fellowship of their group.

The Harvard Project gives special attention to the careful training of highly selected graduate students to become future teachers on the college and seminary level in the field of religion and mental health. The close cooperation between the Harvard Divinity School, the Harvard Medical School, and the Graduate School of Arts and Sciences, especially its department of Social Relations, offers a unique opportunity to men who were already in the ministry, or teaching religion, to acquire the necessary knowledge and skill for a professional career in this area. A three-year program is planned. The first year is concentrated on sharpening the theological, philosophical, and ethical understanding of the Christian faith in the present-day scene. The second year is mainly devoted to giving a thorough acquaintance with the areas of psychology of religion, sociology of religion, and anthropology of religion. The student is also required to relate ethical theories to contemporary problems. The third year is given to an independent research study which leads to a doctoral thesis related to the problem of religion and mental health.

Yeshiva University began its five-year pilot program in February 1957, under Rabbi I. Fred Hollander. Yeshiva is the theological center for Orthodox Judaism in this country, but also is a full university.

The program during the first year of the "pilot project" consisted of a three-hour seminar weekly. For the first half of the weekly meeting, the distinguished Talmudic scholar, Dr. Joseph Soloveitchik, conducted a study of "Problems of Everyday Life," in a lecture course based on Talmudic and other sources. In the second half, the students discussed problems of personality development and life crisis with Rabbi Hollander or the psychiatric consultant to the project. In addition, clinical work was made available to the students under the Institute for Pastoral Psychiatry of the New York Board of Rabbis, directed by Rabbi Hollander.

Yeshiva looks on mental health not as an addition to religion but as an element of it. Psychiatric training is meant to help the clergyman to instill these attitudes and influence the growth or change of personality. Rabbi Hollander (1958) considers the two most important aspects of the program to be "the problem of clarifying the unique role of the clergy in the field of mental health," and "the need to examine some of the differences between psychiatric and religious points of view concerning the factors that contribute to the achievement of mental health."

Of the attempt of the pilot program to reach a standardized curriculum that will integrate the teaching of general principles in the area of mental health with the special functions and educational needs of the clergy, Rabbi Hollander has said:

If this approach is adopted by other institutions on a number of levels, the result should be the elimination of many difficulties now created by individuals who do not play their optimum role in mental health or who attempt to assume functions in this field for which they are inadequately trained. Even more important, this orientation can put to fuller use the age-old resources of religion—newly understood, newly applied, and newly significant.

We talked with Rabbi Hollander about his program, expressing more interest in its goals and in some of its underlying presuppositions than in its content. The Rabbi emphasized three aspects or roles of the clergyman which we must take account of: his ministerial functions, his functions as one who refers people to others, and the function in which he uses his resources to effect personality change or growth. Rabbi Hollander elaborated:

Further, we need to define the types of people he can be most useful to. But modern man in general is not educated to see the clergy as a resource. So we face a double educational problem—clergy and people. We must distinguish further between mental health on the one hand, and psychology on the other. Mental health is a concept man can strive toward; psychology is a tool, as is poetry, philosophy.

These preliminary remarks are necessary in order to appreciate the framework of our program at Yeshiva. In our project on Religion and Mental Health, we offer one course on Judaism's concept of man. If the clergyman has something to offer and is to function, he must have resources, and he must know how to use them.

A related course is given on how to communicate his concept of man. Part of the communication task is understanding the mind. Psychiatric interpretation of growth and development is not enough.

The clergyman needs an understanding of his own field and must be able to make it relevant to the needs of the persons he serves. He needs a religious concept of man which could be applied to the needs of man and help him meet them better (in such areas as belonging, security, purpose, and regarding basic institutions such as the family). He needs a psychiatric understanding which will enable him to communicate this. Finally, he needs a technique. This is hard to communicate because many clergymen do not fully understand what they are trying to do; that is, they have no picture of how they should come to a focus on a problem.

Many people who come to a clergyman are not those he can best help. They come with problems for advice, and not for what they deeply need: meaning and a purpose. The timing of this is important too. For example, the man who has just retired and has found that his life seems to him to have lost its meaning should have been helped to find—or to see—an underlying purpose in his life long before retirement.

Mental health means much more than the absence of mental illness. It means a larger life, it means fulfillment. A wider and deeper interpretation of mental health is needed. The clergy's highest relevance for mental health is in helping to define this wider meaning, and in helping individuals to find it in their own lives. One way is to find new relevance of words and phrases the clergy have been using for years. For example, "purpose" can be seen under two aspects: the kind of purpose without which you cannot live, and the kind of purpose without which you seem to be missing something, life is flat but not impossible. Religion helps to define what goes into a sense of purpose; but the clergy are still confronted with the problem of communicating this. Here is where psychology's greatest contribution—and a key point of intersection between religion and psychology—may be.

Rabbi Joseph B. Soloveitchik (1958), who shares with Rabbi Hollander the direction of the Religion and Mental Health program at Yeshiva, has added, in a conversation with us, some of the underlying philosophy of the program from his own perspective as a scholar of the Talmud:

The theme of our program at Yeshiva is the Judaic approach to human personality. As part of this, we explore the religious resources of the individual in regard to mental health. The mechanics of the program are quite simple. Each week I give a lecture; this is followed by group discussion led by Rabbi Hollander. In a weekly conference together, Rabbi Hollander tells me of problems that arise in the discussions; some of these I integrate into following lectures. Dr. Coleman, a psychiatrist, and Dr. Brown, a cultural anthropologist, also take part in the program.

During the first year of the program, we considered problems of the individual: e.g., loneliness, boredom, death, fear; the emotional life; basic emotions of modern man. The second year we tried to place man in proper perspective, to understand man in the total community, within the patterns of friendship, fellowship, family and the like. It is a practical course, considering how to help man to be as happy and as creative as possible.

Spelling out religious resources in communicable terms is a very hard job. Religion is not a science, but a faith. Our job is one of translation of religious concepts into philosophical and psychological concepts. This is more difficult with regard to Judaism than with Christianity.

Judaism is less interested in purely theological speculation. The question Judaism has asked is, "Who is man who is in search of God?" We try to keep our focus on man, but in relation to God at the ritual level, and in relation to his fellow man at the ethical level.

Thus is developing a "religious philosophical anthropology"—not concerning the descent of man, but concerning the understanding of man. Within this context we then try to understand and deal with man's problems.

Religion should not be interpreted solely in practical terms. It should not make life easier for the congregant. Many times it *makes* problems. We should not approach religion on pragmatic grounds. Today we are too practical. Religion is not electricity, it is a doctrine, a commitment, a philosophy, an adventure. My goal is to find how much of the adventurous there is in the religious personality.

One point of some significance regarding the three "pilot" programs must not be overlooked. The United States Government, through its National Institute of Mental Health grant, has endorsed and supported the exploration of the meeting ground between religion and mental health, as well as the training of clergymen toward greater competence in mental health matters and toward a more profound understanding of man. This felicitous breaching of the traditional barriers between church and state may serve as an example of ways in which two major institutions can come together on issues of common concern.

POST-ORDINATION TRAINING AND EXPERIENCE IN
CLINICAL PASTORAL EDUCATION

The 226,000 members of the "working clergy" of all faiths who have had no clinical training, counseling, or related courses can find many workshops and "refresher courses" in subjects related to mental health. Both secular and religious, both psychological and theological sponsors have conducted symposia, workshops, and other courses or conferences to bring practicing clergymen information and further understanding of mental health matters. The intention of most of these efforts is not to give the pastor a satchel of techniques for dealing with specific problems, but rather to deepen his appreciation of some aspects of mental health and mental illness, to familiarize him with available resources, and to help bring about some changes of attitude toward the mentally ill, toward the troubled, and toward the psychiatric profession.

The Academy of Religion and Mental Health is making a significant contribution to familiarizing clergymen in the parish with principles and problems of mental illness and health. Among the Academy's members are now numbered one-tenth of the country's psychiatrists and a thousand clergymen of all major faiths. Local chapters, or "academy associates," in thirty cities sponsor frequent meetings of small groups of clergymen, psychiatrists, and social scientists. A valuable product of these meetings, besides the psychological insights that will help the clergy in their work, is the contribution they make to the continuing conversation between clergymen and psychiatrists. As the Academy director, the Rev. George Christian Anderson, puts it: "In broadest terms, the work of the Academy is directed toward alleviation of modern man's plague of emotional instability" by recourse to the "integration of the moral values of religion and the scientific insights of psychiatry and the behavioral sciences."

Some clergymen take summer clinical training programs (most of which are not limited to theological students, but include the clergyman who is already in parish work). Mental hospital chaplains conduct one-day conferences for the parish clergy. An example of a more intensive course for the working clergy is the twelve-week course on the pastoral care of the mentally ill sponsored by the Council of Churches of the National Capital Area, conducted at St. Elizabeths Hospital, Washington, D.C., by Chaplain Ernest Bruder, two associate chaplains, and members of the medical staff.

A recent development in pastoral theology is the Institute for Advanced Pastoral Studies at Bloomfield Hills, Michigan. The Institute is a post-ordination training center in the various aspects of the ministry, directed by Reuel L. Howe, formerly professor of Pastoral Theology at The Theological Seminary (Episcopal) in Alexandria, Virginia.

Attendance at the ten-day conferences conducted by the Institute is limited to clergymen, of the several denominations, who have been in the ministry at least three years. The program is geared directly to the needs of the individual participants, who are asked in advance to select the problems they need to explore.

More than one clergyman, after a few years in the parish, begins to be deeply concerned about the meaning of his work, about his own shortcomings in communicating with individuals whose needs may seem remote from his own training and experience. Very often this concern may be accompanied by feelings of ineffectiveness, of frustration, and may become part of an irreducible load of anxiety.

The Institute is a "place to go where he can freely examine his problems and experiences in company with other young ministers who are facing exactly the same kinds of problems." (quoted from *The Man Who Was Cut in Two,* brochure of the Institute.)

Such a resource, although limited to comparatively few pastors each year, will no doubt make its contribution less to developing greater skills and techniques than in fostering the mental health of the pastors themselves.

The Roman Catholic Church directly or indirectly sponsors three institutes or workshops on mental health for pastors in the parish. An Institute for the Clergy on Problems of Pastoral Psychology is held bi-annually at Fordham University. Sponsored by the Department of Psychology at Fordham and financed in part by the New

York State Department of Mental Hygiene, the five-day Institute is open to clergy of all faiths.

The Institute's aims, as defined in the Proceedings of the Second Institute (William Bier, S.J., and A. Schneiders, 1958), are to help the clergy to a better understanding of the emotional problems encountered in pastoral work, to help them handle these more efficiently, to formulate a better understanding and relationship between the clergy and professional psychotherapists, and to evaluate the different approaches to mental health.

An advantage of the Institute's local character—clergymen living in New York State are preferred as participants—is that clergymen who attend come into close contact with psychologists and psychiatrists in their area and learn of the professional resources to which they can resort. Thus referrals, benefiting both parishioners and community, can be made with greater confidence, and often with better timing. The psychologists and psychiatrists receive, in turn, some idea of the perspectives and problems of the clergy.

The second program under Roman Catholic auspices for the "working clergy," the Workshop in Pastoral Counseling at Loras College in Dubuque, Iowa, has been held annually for four years. This program, designed primarily for Roman Catholic clergy, aims at enabling pastors to see where "religious difficulties mask deeper problems of an emotional or neurotic nature." The object which follows from this is a working relationship between clergy and psychiatric resources within the state.

The third program is the Institute on Mental Health at St. John's University in Minnesota, formerly directed by the Rev. Alexius Portz, O.S.B., (and now by the Rev. Gordon Tavis) and one of the outstanding of its kind today.

St. John's is a Benedictine abbey, university, and theological seminary. Its annual Institute, initiated in 1954, is open to all denominations, although it attracts largely Roman Catholic clergy from the Midwestern states. The conferees at the session we attended in the summer of 1958 included two rabbis, five Protestant ministers, and thirty-three Roman Catholic priests. Each of the four summer sessions has a faculty of two lecturers and four seminar leaders; the lecturers at three consecutive summer sessions have included four past presidents of the American Psychiatric Association.

The main object of the institute is "to help clergymen recognize danger signals of mental illness, to deepen their appreciation of mental health aspects of personality development, to increase their means of positive assistance to the ill, to prevent unwitting aggravation of disturbances, and to amplify the role of the clergyman in collaboration with the psychiatric professions." Lectures or general conferences provide basic theoretical and factual knowledge. After each formal session, the students break up into seminars of ten members each, which have been described by the Reverend William McDonnel, O.S.B., (1957):

If the workshop as a whole undergoes the process of group dynamics which is inherent in a learning situation where attitudes and feelings and not mere information are involved, much more so does each seminar group. The first meetings are characterized by a generalized reserve and benevolent skepticism. . . . At the beginning they seem to emphasize the symptomatology of mental disturbance, not infrequently issuing moral judgments they will later recognize as hasty. The seminar leader lets the group work through this introductory stage of dynamics. . . . He extends, qualifies, particularizes the matter of the preceding lecture. He leads the group as it educates itself and turns from concern for identification and classification of mental disease to an understanding of personality development in general, and the cause of personality disorders in particular.

The staff—psychiatrists and psychologists—avoid theoretical controversy on issues which would perplex those untrained in abnormal psychology and attempt, also, to avoid making "pseudo-psychiatrists" of the clergy. Techniques are considered as secondary; what matters is that "there are, ultimately, no techniques, only persons."

The workshops seem to have brought about mutual appreciation and a recognition of their limitations on the part of both psychiatrists and clergymen. The Board of Directors has stated, in evaluating previous sessions: "The psychiatrist quite naturally is preoccupied with the cause of illness. This arises out of his professional dedication to aid the patient in becoming psychologically free or mature. The clergyman is more directly interested in moral and spiritual values, in inspiring the parishioner to use well whatever freedom he has."

A program under medical auspices that interrelates training for the clergy with other disciplines can be seen in the several activities in religion and psychiatry at the Menninger Foundation, Topeka, Kansas. A key feature of the program is that the clergy are not the only participants, but take part along with members of other professions. "An organization such as the Menninger Foundation, which practices, teaches, and promotes psychiatry, is in constant interaction with professional persons and laymen who practice, teach, or promote religion." (Menninger Foundation, 1957.)

Each year the Menninger School of Psychiatry conducts a semester seminar for its Fellows, staff members, and representatives of many professions including the clergy. A course has recently been inaugurated for predoctoral students in Religion and Personality. Both of these are under the direction of Chaplain Thomas W. Klink of the Topeka State Hospital, and Dr. Paul W. Pruyser, clinical psychologist at the Menninger Foundation.

A three-months clinical training program for pastors is conducted by Chaplain Klink and others at the Topeka State Hospital and other institutions. The program is under the sponsorship of the Council for Clinical Training, and relates in many ways with the work of the faculty and Fellows of the Menninger School of Psychiatry. The pastors attend the Menninger seminar on religion and psychiatry and work on "clinical teams" led by both Fellows and alumni of the Menninger School of Psychiatry. The presence of chaplains from the armed services in the Foundation's training program on marriage counseling, the annual Gallahue Seminar on Religion and Psychiatry, the workshops and consultations by Menninger staff members given to religious organizations throughout the country, are further ways in which the Foundation

extends psychiatric training facilities to the clergy, teaching them certain viewpoints and skills helpful in carrying out their pastoral work. On the other hand the Foundation looks to the clergy for help in certain phases of psychiatric treatment—to psychiatric chaplains in mental hospitals, to chaplains in marriage counseling situations, to the parish minister, the priest, or the rabbi in the many phases of outpatient care and inpatient after-care. The Foundation moves in both directions, as do its colleagues in religion. (Menninger Foundation, 1957, p. 70.)

SUMMARY

Of the 235,000 clergymen of all faiths active in parish life (there are an additional 115,000 ordained persons), under 10,000 have taken clinical pastoral training, it is estimated. As we have pointed out, the "clinical training" courses and supervised training programs for theological students and clergymen in hospitals and other institutions are by no means the total content of clinical pastoral education.

It is difficult to give an objective assessment of the programs in clinical pastoral training that we have described, or that have been described especially for this report by their directors. With a few exceptions, such as the testing devised by Father Herr at Loyola University, no practicable procedure or test or other instrument has yet been devised to evaluate the effectiveness of clinical pastoral training, whether specific courses or clinical experiences.

We have noted differences in orientation in these programs; but these differences seem to be only indirectly related to differences in religious background, such as Catholic, Protestant, or Jewish. And we discern some differences in objectives, stated or implied; but we see more difference in the means, the paths to those objectives.

It is important to distinguish trends and themes within the contemporary growth of clinical pastoral training, for this movement cannot by any means be described merely as a haphazard proliferation of courses offered in this field. Some leaders of the movement, for example, see it as an opportunity for providing analytical tools and understanding of psychological principles which can be of general use to the pastor in any application. The larger goal, more predominant in recent years, is seen as the general application of psychological insights to the total range of pastoral activities, rather than emphasis only on the development of counseling skills and on personal therapy for pastors.

Some aim at familiarizing the theological student with the problems of individuals in stress, and have the practical goal of giving him skill and confidence to deal constructively with the emotional and mental problems in the lives of his parishioners. But they invariably add the proviso that part of his training in this area is to give him enough self-knowledge as well as technical understanding to know his limitations, and to know when and how to refer—and to be able to work readily with other professionals.

Some plan as one major goal of the student's training a more profound understanding of man and of himself in a pastoral relationship with others. Towards this end, anthropology, sociology, and other sciences join with psychology to add other dimensions to the student's theological understanding of man. One educator warns that the objective of psychological courses, whether didactic or clinical, in theological education is not to make counselors of theological students, but to increase their understanding of human behavior through knowledge of both psychological and theological dynamics, and so strengthen them in their capacity as clergymen—the goal being effective vocational functioning.

One theological educator describes the goal as not only competence in mental health matters both immediate and long range, but a capacity to aid the parishioner in the development of a wholesome, mature personality, and to help people with what they most deeply need—meaning and purpose in their lives rather than merely help with specific problems.

While some would make the field of pastoral psychology a pivotal point around which other aspects of the theological curriculum can be integrated, we can infer from the evidence we have seen that whether the field of clinical pastoral education is thought of as central or peripheral to the body of theological education in the preparation of the most effective clergy, there is a clearly discernible trend today away from merely developing skills for a problem-centered pastoral ministry. Even predominantly clinical programs are carried on within a much more comprehensive context than "supervised clinical training" per se. A clearly articulated, though not always achieved, objective would seem to be a continual exploration of ways, psychological and otherwise, to help the present and future clergyman, in all aspects of his ministry, to facilitate in the highest possible degree the spiritual *and emotional* growth of his parishioners.

Since we could find no evaluative studies of the church or of the clergy in relation to any aspects of the mental health field, we conducted four related surveys—of mental hospital patients, of laymen, of clergymen, of psychiatrists—in an attempt to bring other perspectives to bear upon this subject.

In Part II, consisting of four chapters, we will present the findings from our four empirical studies and thus provide a mirror in which to see reflected the clergy as they appear to others—and to themselves—as resources for mental health.

PART TWO

Perspectives on the Churches
and Mental Health

VIII

The Mental Hospital Patient Looks at the Chaplain

We take our first perspective on the church in mental health activity by again focusing upon its most intensive and sharply highlighted aspect—namely, its ministry to the mentally ill—and trying to see the chaplain through the eyes of the patients. How do they see him: as a person or as a symbol? Primarily as a secular personage in a position of responsibility, or as a friend, or as a representative of the church? Do the patients feel that he has anything to do with helping them to get well? How has he helped them, and how do they want him to help them?

In seeking answers to such questions, we conducted brief interviews with 200 patients, 100 at each of two State hospitals in the Northeastern section of the country. We went to all wards, from admissions to chronic, and talked with the patients wherever they happened to be at the time, asking the following questions:

1. Who has been most helpful to you in getting to feel better, since coming to the hospital? Why do you mention that person? In what way has he been most helpful to you?

2. When was the last time you spoke with one of the doctors here at the hospital?

3. Do you ever see the chaplains here at the hospital? When was the last time you spoke to one of them?

4. What sort of thing did you talk about with the chaplain? Where did you talk with the chaplain? Did you go to see him, or did he come to see you?

5. Are there any ways in which the chaplain has helped you since you've come to the hospital?

6. Are there any ways in which you would like him to help you?

7. What church did you belong to before coming to the hospital? Has the pastor from your church at home ever come to visit you here in the hospital?

The first hospital, which we will call Midville State Hospital, has about 1800 patients, with a Catholic-Protestant patient ratio of about 3 to 2. There are two Roman Catholic chaplains, and one Protestant. A Jewish chaplain comes to the hospital once or twice a week to serve the patients of the Jewish faith. A Roman Catholic chapel has recently been constructed on the grounds of Midville. The second hospital, which we will call Westland State Hospital, has approximately 2400 patients and a similar Catholic-Protestant patient ratio. At Westland, one Protestant and one Roman Catholic chaplain, as well as a visiting rabbi, serve the 2400 patients.

We realized that some patients would be more or less out of contact, and that others would refuse to answer some or all of the questions. In the course of reaching our objective of 200 patient interviews, we approached an additional 55 patients, 19 men and 36 women, who either refused to answer or were severely dissociated, and who are not included in this discussion.

DESCRIPTION OF THE PATIENTS

We interviewed 112 women and 88 men. Of the women, 45 were single, 46 married, 21 separated, divorced, or widowed. Of the men, 47 were single, 33 married, and 8 separated, divorced, or widowed—a total of both sexes of 92 single, 79 married, and 29 separated, divorced, or widowed.

Forty-four patients of the 200 had an education of grade school or less; 63 had from one to four years of high school; 14 had had some college education or a college degree. Two had taken graduate work. The educational level of 77 of the 200 patients was not on the hospital records.

In showing the occupations of the 200 patients, rather than the usual categories of skilled, semi-skilled, unskilled, and the like, we have used more descriptive terms. Beginning with professional and semi-professional, of whom there were 10, the patients included 18 clerical and sales workers, 18 craftsmen, 6 service workers, and 44 laborers of various kinds. In addition, there were 35 housewives, 8 students, and 30 retired or unemployed. The occupations of 31 patients were not listed in the hospital records.

Of the 200 patients, 111 were Roman Catholic, 71 Protestant, 7 Jewish, 3 Greek Orthodox, and 8 had no affiliation. This division among major faith groups in our respondents reflects roughly the ratio for the hospitals as a whole, and also for the communities from which they draw their patients. Fifty-two of the 71 Protestants were members of traditional churches (Congregational, Baptist, and Episcopal being most frequent); six were members of small sects; 13 indicated no choice of denomination.

The length of hospitalization varied among these 200 patients from 15 who had been in the hospital for less than one month to one who had been there 32 years. A total of 26 had been patients for two months or less; 28, between two months and one year; 27, from one to three years; 28, from three to six years; 30, from six to twelve years; 37, from twelve to twenty years; and 24 for twenty-four years and more. As the chaplains make a practice of interviewing new patients, patients who had been hospitalized for a short time would be likely to say they had seen the chaplain recently, and be likely to remember what they had talked about. On the other hand, short-term patients would be less likely than others to have occasion for the chaplain to be helpful to them in specific ways. Long-term patients were more likely to be on "back" or chronic wards, and thus the chaplain's contact with them was likely to be a factor of his degree of industry and sheer rate of travel.

Of our 200 respondents, 123 had been diagnosed as schizophrenic (including paranoid schizophrenic), 14 paranoid, and 30 depressed. There were 27 with diagnoses of organic brain diseases, and 6 undiagnosed.

THE PATIENTS' RESPONSES

When asked "Who has been most helpful to you in getting to feel better since coming to the hospital?" a fourth of the patients said, "No one," or "Myself," or "I don't know" (see Table 1). The most frequent positive response was "the doctor," or "the doctors" (47). Seven gave both doctors and nurses, and 25 named nurses and attendants. Forty-four thought that the staff as a whole had given them the most help. Ten thought the most help had come from other patients, and eight mentioned family and friends. Nine chose a religious source.

It is useful to note the general trend of these responses in order to see their relation to the 9 responses referring to religion: "The chaplain" (5—in each case, a Roman Catholic chaplain), "God" (3), and "My faith" (1).

This first question was phrased in such a way that we might well have anticipated answers in a medical rather than a religious context. In asking this question, we may not have tapped the patients' feelings about the importance to them of the chaplain and others *in general,* but only in the limited sense of "helping them get to feel better." Furthermore, the patients did not know that they would be asked about the chaplain in further questions. Hence, though only 5 out of 200 patients chose the chaplain, and 3 said God, and one said

Table 1—Persons Seen by Patients as Most Helpful

Persons	Midville	Westland	Total
No one (or myself, or I don't know)	17	33	50
The doctor or doctors	31	16	47
The doctors and nurses	4	3	7
Nurses and attendants	11	14	25
Whole staff[a]	24	20	44
Other patients	3	7	10
Family, friends or others[b]	5	3	8
The chaplains, God, or my faith[c]	5	4	9
	100	100	200

[a] Including dentist (1) and social worker (1).
[b] Responses include five specific mentions of the patient's family or family members, and one mention of a visiting student participant in a volunteer program.
[c] Chaplains (5); God (3); My Faith (1). See text.

"My faith," we can be fairly confident that these answers reflect the way they really feel on the subject. Whether the chaplain has *in fact* been most helpful in getting these five patients to feel better is another matter; it is what the patients think about it that is the object of our inquiry.

The impression of the minor importance of the chaplain for the patient, at least in the process of getting to feel better, is reflected in some findings in a study conducted by Simon Olshansky and Samuel Grob under the joint sponsorship of the Office of Vocational Rehabilitation and the Massachusetts Association for Mental Health. One hundred and sixty former mental patients were interviewed from three to five years after their discharge. Among the questions asked was one similar to our first one, as to who had been of most help. None of the 160 patients selected the chaplain. One mentioned having received help during the period since his discharge from a Roman Catholic priest, who aided him in contacting a psychiatrist.

After naming the most helpful person, our patients were asked: "Why do you mention that person? In what way has he (or she) helped you?" (see Table 2). Eighty-one patients responded in what we have called "interpersonally supportive" terms. Their responses include such statements as, "She's very nice and friendly" (referring to a nurse); "The hospital routine helps, and the things they give you to do"; "The nurses are here and they help you—they are the boss." Twenty patients described the help they have received in terms that we have categorized as "instrumental": "They take us to entertainments"; "They buy clothes for us"; "He finds jobs for me to do"; "He helped me go home at Christmas."

These responses may seem to be rather tangential reasons for the choice of the one who has done most to help the patient get to feel better. Though they may be isolated and individual actions with

Table 2—Types of Help From Most Helpful Persons

No one has helped me	50
Nothing specific	7
Interpersonally supportive	81
Medical treatment	42
Instrumental	20
	200

seemingly not much bearing on the total healing process, they may be symbolic of the continuing relationship and are the readily describable symbolic aspects of it that the patient brings to mind.

Some of the reasons for selecting the chaplain, as given by the five patients who referred to him as the most helpful, are as follows: A seventy-four-year old woman, diagnosed as schizophrenic, replied: "The priest. He talks very nicely to me. He hears my confession. He helps me because I am a great believer in the Roman Catholic faith." A thirty-three-year old housewife, diagnosed as paranoid schizophrenic and hospitalized for three months: "The priest. Confession is good for the soul." A thirty-two-year old single woman (dementia praecox, three years hospitalized) included Father D. with the doctors and attendants. "They all give me cigarettes and ward work," she said. A seventy-eight-year old former musician (paranoid schizophrenia, hospitalized twenty years) included both "almighty God and the priests" as having helped him most. "The priestly duties give me strength and bring me closer to God."

Four patients replied in a religious context without making specific reference to the chaplain. "My faith," said a forty-year old schizophrenic textile worker. "I'm a Catholic and I went to parochial school; that stays with you." A twenty-nine-year old restaurant worker with a diagnosis of chronic undifferentiated schizophrenia: "God helps me to help myself. God keeps me from cracking up most of the time." A twenty-eight-year old housewife, hospitalized one month with a diagnosis of schizophrenia: "God, having faith in God. The psychiatrist has helped me to relieve my conscience. If it weren't for God we wouldn't be here in this life." A seventy-four-year old woman, single, diagnosed as hebephrenic schizophrenic, and hospitalized twenty-four years: "God helps me most, the poor man. I don't know what to do for him. He helps me to get by."

Two-thirds of the patients had talked with a doctor during the past month, and one-half had talked with a chaplain during the past month (see Tables 3 and 4). Greater frequency, or at least greater recency, of patient-doctor conversations is apparent. Yet in view of the doctor-to-chaplain ratio in the two hospitals, it is somewhat surprising that the contrast is not still greater.

Table 3—Time of Most Recent Doctor-Patient Conversation

	Total
Within the past week	72
Within the past month	61
Within the past year	27
Over a year ago	20
Never	5
Don't remember	15

Table 4—Time of Most Recent Chaplain-Patient Conversation

	Total
Within the past week	58
Within the past month	42
Within the past year	45
Over a year ago	12
Never	40
Don't remember	3

"What did you talk about with the chaplain?" Besides the patients who said they had never talked with the chaplain (40), or who did not answer this question (9), the remainder are nearly equally divided between those whose conversational content was of secular nature (72), and those who expressed some religious concern (79) (Table 5). We have used the word "instrumental" as a convenient term to indicate utilitarian and personal services, favors, errands, and the like. Instrumental help includes such responses as "I asked him to get me out of here"; "I asked him to contact my family." "Interpersonal-supportive" material includes such replies as "We talked about the weather"; "We just passed the time of day." "We just said hello." The majority of the sixty-six in this group just said hello. "Instrumental as chaplain" would include asking for some service that he would be likely to do only in his capacity as a chaplain. "Supportive as a chaplain": "He told me we have to make the best of our circumstances." "We talked about the meaning of Yom Kippur." (Further clarification and examples of these terms will be given when we discuss the answers to Questions 5 and 6.)

Most of these exchanges took place on the ward. Nearly half were initiated by the chaplain, and a fourth by the patients. Most seem to have been brief exchanges rather than conversations of any duration. We did not press the patients to tell us about more in-

Table 5—Content of Chaplain-Patient Conversations

	Midville	Westland	Total
Never talked (40), or no reply (9)	19	30	49
Asking instrumental help	4	2	6
Interpersonal-supportive material	31	35	66
Religious concerns			
Instrumental as a chaplain	1	3	4
Supportive as a chaplain	19	13	32
The services of the church	26	17	43
	100	100	200

tensive or prolonged talks with the chaplain, for we felt that some Roman Catholic patients might misunderstand and think we were inquiring about matters disclosed only to the priest during confession. However, no patients happened to mention confession as the last occasion on which they talked with the chaplain.

"Are there any ways in which the chaplain has helped you since you've come to the hospital?"

Half of the patients answered "No," or "Nothing" (Table 6). Thirty-two saw the chaplain's help in secular terms; of these, five were what we have called instrumental, or mediary—what any layman with some influence or connections with the staff or with the "outside" might have done for them. Twenty-seven saw the help of the chaplain as what we have termed "supportive as a person"— what any person could do for them who wanted to stop long enough. "He's very friendly; some people go through and never say hello." "It's nice to have someone to talk to." "It's nice to talk to people like that, they brace you up with a little kindness." "He

Table 6—Chaplain's Help Received

	Midville	Westland	Total
No help	47	53	100
Secular help			
Instrumental person	0	5	5
Supportive person	17	10	27
Total	17	15	32
Religious help			
Instrumental as a chaplain	1	3	4
Supportive as a chaplain	21	18	39
Ritualistic (Church services)	14	11	25
Total	36	32	68
	100	100	200

helped me by talking to me." In neither of these secular aspects—
the mediator or the supportive—did the patient see the help he has
received as anything exclusively characteristic of the chaplain's role
or identity.

Sixty-eight patients described in a religious context the ways in
which the chaplain had helped them. The four responses we have
described as "instrumental as a chaplain" include such ways as: "He's
given me a new prayer book every year"; "He wrote to my home
minister." Thirty-nine saw him as "supportive as a chaplain": "He's
given me faith," "He kept me from breaking up when my mother
died." "He prays." "I don't see him often enough; it's a relief to see
him." "He gives you a better perspective. I'd rather talk five minutes
with the priest than three hours with the psychiatrist."

Of the sixty-eight who described the chaplain's help in a religious
context, twenty-five referred specifically to the liturgical aspects of
the chaplain's work—the services of the church—as the way in which
he had helped them. "I used to get a blessing out of his services; the
talks he'd have and the singing." "The beauty of the church has
helped me." "I need confession and communion." "It makes you
feel good to go to church." "He's helped me with his sermons."
"Nothing outside of going to church."

When asked, "Are there any ways in which you would like the
chaplain to help you?" 111 patients answered "No," or "None," or
"Can't think of any" (Table 7). Four of these could be described as
strongly anticlerical or antireligious. A sixty-two-year old male
patient said, "No. Nothing. I studied religion and found it false."

Table 7—Chaplain's Help Wanted

	Medville	Westland	Total
No help	54	57	111
Secular help			
Instrumental person	22	17	39
Supportive person	3	3	6
Total	25	20	45
Religious help			
Instrumental as chaplain	2	6	8
Supportive as chaplain	16	11	27
Ritualistic (church activities)	3	6	9
Total	21	23	44
	100	100	200

A sixty-seven-year old housewife said, "Just keep him away from me. I had enough religion when I was young."

Forty-five patients saw the chaplain's potential and future help in secular terms. Of these, twenty-five wanted him to "get me out of here," "send me home for good." An additional fourteen, who are included with the twenty-five in the instrumental or mediation category, wanted the chaplain to do specific things for them, such as secure more reading matter, a suit of clothes, arrange work outside, "Tell Dr. Jim I'm improving," arrange for a job after release, contact wife, "Come around more often and give the boys a cigarette." Six of the forty-five wanted help which we have described as supportive, though still in secular terms.

Forty-four wanted religious help. Eight of these were in instrumental or mediator terms, such as "I'd like him to help place my children in a Catholic home," "Get religious articles for me to read," "I'd like to go to the downtown churches again" (referring to a visit when accompanied by the chaplain).

Twenty-seven wanted future help from the chaplain in what we have called supportive ways. Fourteen of these wanted him to pray for them (compared with one who referred to prayer when asked about previous help received from the chaplain). Others: "I would like him to keep up my good faith." "I would like to continue to confide in him; he's very comforting." "Give me advice. They're educated, and have an answer for everything." "It would help if he was with us in EST and for operations, praying for us and guiding us." "Just carrying on as he is. He's spiritually uplifting. I can bare my soul to him."

Nine patients referred to the services conducted by the chaplain as ways they would like him to help in the future. "I want to go to communion, but they never tell me to go." "I'd like to hear Mass." "I'd just like to continue to practice my religion." "Give me good advice in confession."

A comparison of ways in which patients think the chaplains have helped, and ways in which they can help, for the future, can be seen in Table 8. More than twice as many think of the chaplain's previous (actual) help in religious as in secular terms. For future

Table 8—Comparison of Chaplain's Help Received and Wanted

	WAYS IN WHICH THE CHAPLAIN			
	Has Helped (actual)		Can Help (ideal)	
None		100		111
Secular help				
Instrumental	5		39	
Supportive	27		6	
Total		32		45
Religious help				
Instrumental	4		8	
Supportive	39		27	
Ritualistic (church services)	25		9	
Total		68		44
		200		200

help, the secular and religious are even (the secular raised by the large proportion who want him to get them out). In going from past to future, from actual to ideal, the secular-supportive shifts from 27 to 6. The ritualistic (help seen in the services of the church) declines from 25 who value this as the chaplain's past help, to 9 who see it as the help they value most from him in the future. The least change occurs in the religious-supportive: 39 past (actual) to 27 future (ideal). While the secular and religious ways in which the chaplain can help in the future are evenly balanced, when the 25 patients who want the chaplain to get them discharged and the 111 who want no help are accounted for, the largest number of patients are seen to want the chaplain to be what he is, a chaplain, a pastor, and to have a personal (rather than an official or ritualistic) relationship with them, one in which they find support and guidance and understanding.

The 39 patients who saw the previous help of the chaplain in supportive religious terms gave the smallest percentage of those who want no help, and the largest percentage of those who want religious help. Only two of the 25 who saw the chaplain's past help in terms of the church service visualize his future help in ritualistic ways. We also note a strong association between having received some help from the chaplain, and wanting some help (this trend is stronger among male than among female patients). Among the few patients who want services of the church—that is, who see the chaplain's future help in ritualistic or institutional terms—young patients predominate.

During the period, brief or prolonged, when these patients are away from their communities and homes and churches and while their spiritual care is more or less officially entrusted to the hospital chaplain, what relation have they had with the pastors of their own churches?

Twenty-two of these 200 patients reported that they had been visited by the pastor of their home church. Almost all of these were Protestant. While some may not have remembered a visit from their home pastor, this figure of barely over 10 per cent seems to indicate a rather low contact rate between parish clergymen and hospitalized parishioners, and a low degree of participation by the "outside" clergy in that aspect of the mental health field symbolized by the mental hospital. Some patients, of course, may have stopped attending church and drifted away from contact with any religious group long before they were hospitalized. Also, some have been hospitalized for a great number of years. Thus, on either count, visits from their home clergyman would undoubtedly represent for some patients a resumption, even an initiation, of a pastoral relationship rather than its continuation. However, many chaplains have expressed their distress at finding reluctance on the part of the patients' own clergymen to visit them in the hospital, and also at observing the attitude on the part of outside clergymen that hospitalization seems to make the spiritual welfare of their parishioners the exclusive concern of the hospital chaplain.

We do not know the extent of the "impact" of the chaplains on patients in mental hospitals throughout the country, nor their impact on the remaining 3800 patients we did not interview in the two hospitals selected. Some of the findings we have presented here as a result of our interviews with 200 patients may give the chaplain another perspective from which to view himself, to catch his image as it is reflected in the eyes of the patients, to see in what ways he can be of most help to them.

Half of the patients we interviewed saw the chaplain as having given them help of some kind, and for over two-thirds of these, the greatest help seemed to the patients to be within a religious rather than a secular context. It was within the scope of his role as a chaplain that they valued him most highly. Forty-five per cent of the patients wanted help from the chaplain in the future, and of these, half wanted this help to be within a religious framework. They wanted the chaplain to be not a therapist, not a "member of the team," not a mediating layman, but a chaplain, a pastor, with a sustaining supportive relationship to them.

The negative aspects of some of these findings must not be glossed over: half of the patients said they got no help from the chaplain, and over half wanted no help. Nor can we ignore the negative finding that only five out of 200 patients—2.5 per cent—saw the chaplain as an important resource in getting to feel better. Of course, the optimist can read this with another emphasis: as many as 2.5 per cent see the chaplain as such a resource. Yet the realist will place this finding beside the incontrovertible facts that there are few chaplains and many mental hospital patients.

IX

Religion and Mental Health in Two Communities

ALTHOUGH THE scope of our project, and the time available for it, precluded systematic field studies, we undertook some exploratory interviews with laymen in two communities, one in the Northeast and one in the Midwest. These interviews provide the basis for our second perspective.

We wanted to find out what people would tell us more or less spontaneously about their religious beliefs, about their problems, about the two principal ways of dealing with problems—coping with them or getting help for them—and their feelings about sources of help, such as the clergyman and the psychiatrist. Further, we hoped to learn if there would be any observable differences, in these sentiments, among people of quite different socioeconomic backgrounds.

The sheer availability of mental health resources does not always mean that people will avail themselves of them. Many barriers stand between the resource and the individual in need. Even in a city with good mental health facilities and resources, social and cultural distance, such as might be characteristic of a deteriorating residential area surviving in the inner city, could make psychiatric help just as inaccessible as could geographic distance. An analogous reservation can be made regarding the clergy. Though the clergy outnumber psychiatrists 35 to one, and thus might be thought to be more accessible to people in trouble, laymen's attitudes toward the clergy may block recourse to them in time of need.

[154]

The sentiments expressed here by respondents in two communities give us some feeling for the religious beliefs, the problems, and the attitudes toward clergy and toward psychiatrists on the part of ordinary people. Our interviewees are not experts on religion or experts on mental health, but businessmen, laborers, housewives. What they have to say about their religious beliefs seems to be less formal and doctrinal than individual and personalized, and so might be considered a kind of "folk religion." And what they say about their problems and the ways they deal with them can be seen as a kind of "folk psychology." Both the "folk religion" and the "folk psychology" provide still another perspective from which we may view various dimensions of the relation between religion and mental health, the church's resources and activities in the area of mental health, and people's responses to what the churches have to offer.

We conducted interviews of about an hour's duration each with a total of 160 people, some in a large eastern city, which we will call Northboro, others in a small midwestern manufacturing and dairying center, which we will call Centerboro. In addition to questions about immediate family members, we asked our respondents about certain aspects of their religious beliefs, their perception of the clergy (with whom most had some contact), their personal problems, and their perception of the psychiatrist (with whom most had no contact).

Our respondents were men and women of varying ages, occupations, and religious affiliation—Catholic, Protestant, and Jewish— as well as of widely varying educational and socioeconomic levels. We thus got some variety of respondents, though limited to those who were ready and willing to talk. While no findings from these interviews are to be generalized to a larger population, it seems fair and possible to draw some inferences from the material and to raise some questions.

Northboro, with its surrounding suburban towns, is a metropolitan complex of over a million inhabitants, and a major center for industry, trade, and transportation. Several universities and colleges are located in the city or in its immediate vicinity. One-half the population is Roman Catholic, one-tenth Jewish.

The section of Northboro in which we conducted the interviews reported here is a severely deteriorated inner-city area partially isolated by surrounding industrial development. In one direction it is cut off from the rest of the city by railway yards; in another, by factories. The majority of the interviewees in this area were marginal workers, with only the most elementary public or parochial school education, and living in poor material circumstances. A number were receiving unemployment benefits at the time we talked with them, or were dependent on other help for subsistence. Their average age was thirty-six. Three-fourths of our Northboro respondents were Roman Catholic, the rest Protestant (20 per cent) and Jewish (5 per cent).

We talked with some of these people in their homes, some on their front steps where many sit, alone or in groups, on warm evenings. Four interviews took place in a neighborhood tavern. Most of those approached assented readily to an interview. The few who refused didn't think they could be of any help, or weren't interested in being interviewed by anyone, or were too busy.

RELIGIOUS BELIEFS

Belief in God, no matter how defined, seemed to play a significant part in the world or life view of most of the people with whom we talked. The existence of God did not always have a describable bearing upon the individual's life or conduct; but many felt that God was, in any case, a necessary presence.

In no instance did we find any atheistic, agnostic, or uncertain sentiment concerning the existence of God and the necessity of His presence. Our informants spoke of a personal God ("He's always with you."), a protective and fatherly God, an accessible God ("If you're in trouble, you go to Him."), a compassionate God.

Belief in God was accompanied by a belief in the hereafter, particularly by those informants who attended church frequently.

And most individuals reported that they tried to conduct their life on earth in such a fashion as to make possible "a future meeting with God and existence with Him in an after-life for all eternity."

Doctrinal delineation of God, Jesus, or Mary was either entirely absent or of the most primitive kind. For example, God was simply God, Jesus was at most the Son of God (for Protestants) or God (for Roman Catholics), and Mary the Mother of our Lord, or the Mother of Christ. Only one informant spoke of Jesus in a more elaborate fashion: "He's the First Priest of the Church."

Among many informants strength of belief seemed to be closely related to frequency of church attendance. Among those, however, who did not attend church frequently, the existence of God seemed to be just as meaningful, in that they could not envision a world bereft of God.

When asked what they thought the world would be like if there were no God, most informants felt that either the world would not exist or if it did, it would be a wholly unenviable place in which to live. Almost a third of the informants felt that there would be no world since God had created all things. Of those who felt the world would continue to exist, most thought it would be "a sad place" or "a dangerous place." A frequent reason given for this opinion was the belief that God was the source of order in society and in the individual's private life. God held chaotic forces in check and without Him, life would be characterized by eternal conflict, "corruption," and "persecution" of peoples. Crimes would increase, dictators would reign, "bad men and devils would come into control of government," and "people would succumb to temptation." Furthermore, since God is the wellspring of pity and human dignity as well as the source of private and public morality, without Him there would be only personal selfishness. As one informant put it, life would be Hell.

A third of the informants could not conceive of losing their belief in God. Another third felt that if they were to do so, they would have nothing to live for. "Without God," as one expressed it, "my life would simply be empty." "Not to believe in God would separate you from all human kind." "I would be immoral." "My main source of appeal and help would be gone." "I would lose the respect of my children, since I have taught them always to believe in God."

PERCEPTION OF THE PASTOR

When asked about their pastor, Roman Catholic respondents often indicated that they didn't know the priest well enough to speak informatively about him. A frequent response to this question was, "Which one? There are four of them over there." Personal acquaintance with the clergyman often depended on the frequency of the informant's church attendance. Catholics who attended church frequently were more likely than infrequent attenders to speak of one priest whom they knew better than another (there were several on the staff of the church which most of our Catholic informants attended), to say that they had consulted a priest for advice, and to suggest that they might consult a priest in the future if need arose.

People who had gone to a priest or minister for advice in the past had done so for a number of reasons: for a job; for references; because drinking had become a problem, either for themselves or for a member of their family; occasionally because of difficulty with their children; or because of marital problems. The clergyman to whom the Roman Catholic informants had gone for help was usually not just an anonymous member of the church's staff contacted by chance from among those who happened to be available at the time. On the contrary, people had selected a particular priest because he was friendly, easy to talk with, accessible, or actively interested in the personal needs of his parishioners.

If parishioners did not consult priest or minister when they had a problem, it was frequently because they did not consider the problem of such a nature as to require consulting another. Some felt that they could solve their problems either by understanding them or by praying for help in solving them. Prayer is fairly common among these respondents, for both frequent and infrequent churchgoers.

Some individuals had always dealt with their problems by themselves, never taking the initiative of going to a priest or minister although they felt it might have been helpful to do so. A few felt that another agency could be of greater service (e.g., one informant, an alcoholic, felt that Alcoholics Anonymous could be of greater help to him than could a priest).

If there was a barrier to consulting a clergyman, it was likely to be the result of one or two factors: some concrete situation in which the clergyman did not warrant the confidence of the parishioner, being perceived as having failed him once before; or a situation in which the informant did not feel he knew the priest or minister well enough to take the liberty of consulting him. Anti-clericalism seems not to be a factor determining whether or not the individual would go to a priest or minister for advice. In one instance, a Roman Catholic informant was outspokenly critical of the idea that a priest might have some special distinction as a member of the clergy. Indeed, most informants, in speaking of the priest, tended to refer to him in personal rather than institutional or ecclesiastical terms, and to think of him as a person, rather than as an official of the Church. Respect for the priest seemed to depend upon his personal qualities; the individual would go for help to that priest who, he felt, would be personally receptive to him.

PROBLEMS

About a third of the informants felt that they didn't have any problems. And more than a third spoke of their problems as financial ones. A few of the informants recognized drinking to constitute a problem; others spoke of physical illness.

Several respondents felt loneliness to be a problem, although they often used other terms to describe their situation. Loneliness may be a factor of the anonymity and dislocation that sometimes are characteristic of the urban center, intensified in the lives of these people by the physical deterioration and isolation of their little residential pocket in an industrialized area.

PERCEPTION OF THE PSYCHIATRIST

Only three of the informants had ever felt the need to go to a psychiatrist or psychologist, and none of them had gone. One, an alcoholic who suffered anxiety when in a crowd, felt that the psychiatrist or psychologist could be of no help to him. Another had never made up his mind to go. A moody, nervous woman whose friends had suggested that she have psychiatric help of some kind had gone to a priest instead. Of those who had never felt the need to go to a psychiatrist or psychologist, several made qualifying statements to the effect that they didn't believe in psychology or psychiatry, or that they felt the psychiatrist or psychologist had his own problems, too. Several informants stated that even if they thought they needed help, they had no money for such treatment.

When asked what they thought the psychiatrist or psychologist does when he sees a patient, the informants gave a variety of answers. About one-third didn't know. A considerable number thought that the psychiatrist or psychologist explores the patient's past "in order to learn his case history"; only a few of the informants who thought this said that the psychiatrist or psychologist would then be of help to the patient. Several thought the psychiatrist or psychologist gave advice to the patient. A considerable number felt that the psychiatrist treated only people with serious mental illnesses which so disrupted an individual's existence as to necessitate hospitalization.

Centerboro, the other area in which we conducted interviews, is a community of 40,000 located near the geographic center of the United States. It is 65 miles from the nearest large city. Chief industries are papermilling, granite cutting, and the manufacture of refrigerators, although the economy of the area is distinctively rural. The three surrounding counties are noted for dairying and diversified farming; many Centerboro residents are retired farmers. The predominant social stratification is in the upper-lower and upper-middle brackets. Approximately 70 per cent of the population is Roman Catholic.

Medical facilities include a number of clinics and a Catholic hospital. There is a local chapter of Alcoholics Anonymous, a Catholic Marriage Counseling Service, and the usual County health and welfare services. Although there is no resident psychiatrist in Centerboro, psychiatric consultation is available at the Marriage Counseling Service in the office of the Bureau of Catholic Charities. Counseling services by professional psychologists are available at the State College.

We have selected interviews from respondents who live in a forty-eight-square block area in the vicinity of the State College. This section of the city includes the small percentage of "old-line" families in the upper-middle and lower-upper brackets, and in general reflects a higher educational and socioeconomic level than other areas of the city. This section also has the highest percentage of Protestants in a predominantly Roman Catholic city.

We were, of course, interested in regional variations insofar as they may affect attitudes and values; yet regional variations were minimal when compared with variations determined by class levels. Hence we selected interviews from this upper-middle section of Centerboro as a possible contrast to the preceding group of interviews from the economically depressed area of Northboro—thus representing extremes of the socioeconomic spectrum.

With two or three exceptions, all Centerboro interviewees were in the lower-middle or upper-middle socioeconomic classifications. Ages ranged from twenty to seventy-five; more than half the respondents were over forty-five. The average age was forty-six. All but two had gone beyond high school. Occupations included educator, student, printer, insurance salesman, youth counselor, social worker, librarian, paper mill manager, oil company district manager, physician, housewife. Sixty per cent were Protestant, representing seven denominations; 40 per cent were Roman Catholic.

RELIGIOUS BELIEFS

The Roman Catholic respondents seemed to subscribe more or less fully to the Church's teaching about central doctrinal matters, such as God, Jesus, Mary, and after-life. The Protestant respondents were in general less clear and specific in stating their beliefs concerning the major creedal concepts. Almost all of the Protestant informants reflected ideas of God as the Supreme Being who has created not only Man but a life plan for him, and guides him as he tries to live according to it.

All the Catholics and half the Protestants affirmed the divinity of Christ. Almost all professed belief in some kind of after-life, although few of either Catholic or Protestant respondents expressed the conception of heaven as a place of reward for a virtuous life. Two explained their belief in the after-life as a continuation of the effect of one's life now, a kind of "immortality of influence." Three others described a kind of continuation in which there is no individual identity or awareness but an absorption into the totality of existence. One defined the "life everlasting" as a quality—rather than a time—which is also present now. Protestant informants generally did not believe in the existence of hell and purgatory.

When asked what their own lives would be like if they lost all belief in God, half of the respondents could not attempt to describe this hypothetical situation. Of those who answered, some felt they would then have no purpose in life. One expressed it this way: "If that should happen, I'd no longer know why I was living." Another said, "I would just feel empty." A Lutheran housewife answered, "I wouldn't know *how* to live." One respondent, after thinking over the question for some time, frankly stated that in such a circumstance she could probably find "a substitute person or object to worship."

Loss of belief, for most respondents, seemed to be related to loss of purpose and loss of guidance for the conduct of one's life.

PERCEPTION OF THE PASTOR

In describing their pastor, most of the interviewees stated that they knew him only insofar as they see and hear him in church on Sundays. Some referred to other associations with their pastor, such as business contacts or church society membership. Few interviewees had gone to their priest or minister for help. Common reasons given by Catholics are that the assistant priests at the Cathedral are shifted so rapidly that it is difficult to rely upon one man as an advisor, and that the priests seemed to be too busy. Two Catholics felt that their priests should have more training in pastoral psychology. Three Protestant respondents felt that their clergyman's method of presentation of religious beliefs in church made them hesitate to consult him privately.

Some respondents had been helped by talking with clergymen with experience in marriage counseling; others referred to help they had received in times of bereavement. Search for emotional consolation seemed to be a common theme, stated or implied in many interviews. It might be related to the fact that for many people the most important aspect of religion is trust in God, and only secondarily do they seem concerned about dogma and theology. Many interviewees seemed to have a very hazy doctrinal knowledge of their own faith.

Somewhat over one-half of the informants stated or implied that they would go to a clergyman for help if the situation warranted. Several definitely indicated that they would not go even if they felt they might benefit. A frequent reason given was that they were confident that they could handle their problems by themselves.

While a large number said they would go to see a spiritual advisor if the situation called for it, none could explain in detail what such a situation would be. When we posed hypothetical situations, most still hesitated to commit themselves and said that they would have to be in the situation actually to know how they would react. A few said that they would probably have to be told to consult a spiritual counselor by someone else, such as a friend, who might have a better perspective of the problem.

PROBLEMS

The majority of respondents indicated that all their problems had been of such a nature that they would not classify them as serious. The remainder referred to some upsetting crises or problems in their lives, including the death of relatives, personality problems in child-parent or husband-wife relationships, and problems of an economic nature.

The majority of our respondents preferred initially to handle their difficulties by themselves. For all the married couples this included talking the problem out with their spouse. Many had found prayer to be a great help in dealing with both emotional and spiritual problems. Several respondents suggested preparation for handling stressful situations through education and "mental preparation." In cases where the death of a relative was foreseen, for example, the mental shock was greatly reduced.

Several respondents offered suggestions for extending potential resources, such as educating prospective teachers in spotting mental and emotional disturbance, and making better use of the mass media of communication to educate people as to solutions for these problems.

PERCEPTION OF THE PSYCHIATRIST

Somewhat less than one-half of the Centerboro respondents said they would definitely seek psychiatric aid of some sort if they felt they needed it. Only three were opposed to going to a psychiatrist or a psychologist, one reason for this reluctance being fear of what others would say. The financial difficulty involved in psychiatric care was mentioned as an obstacle even by those who would otherwise be amenable to using such aid.

Several respondents pointed to the family doctor as a source of psychiatric and pre-psychiatric help as well as an alternative to it. In many cases they felt he could help them over a mental or emotional difficulty if it weren't too advanced.

Most interviewees had rather clear impressions as to what psychiatry and psychology have to offer the mentally or emotionally disturbed, and as to what the psychiatrist does to help his patients. However, they seemed to be largely unaware of the extent to which these resurces are available in Centerboro, or where auxiliary mental health services are to be found.

SUMMARY

Before summarizing the impressions we have drawn from our interviews in Northboro and Centerboro, we call attention to the nature of the responses to an area of our interviews not reported here: namely, perception of family members. We asked questions about the respondents' families so that we could note the respondents' perception of important figures in their lives, such as the pastor, within the context of their perception of other figures. In the low socioeconomic area of Northboro, we got quite bare, sparse responses regarding parents and children, and somewhat fuller responses regarding the spouse. Descriptions of parents were frequently expressed in the form of adjectival staccatos: "A good-natured man. Hard-working. Strict." Even after probe questions (e.g., What else could you tell me about your father?), the informants generally limited themselves to simple descriptive terms with little attempt to elaborate their answers. In talking about their children, most informants were also brief and laconic. However, in describing their spouses, the respondents spoke more fully; their descriptions showed more perceptiveness, more awareness of the spouse as a distinct person. "My husband is a good man. He used to bring his wages home . . . until he got sick. Now he's moody, but you got to expect that. Now that he has that heart ailment he feels sorry for himself."

Although our interviewees in the higher socioeconomic area of Centerboro expressed themselves more freely and fully on all topics than did the Northboro residents, a similar distinction could be observed there also. If what people say about members of their immediate families reflects their perception of those family members, and their relationship and communication with them, we can infer that, for the individuals with whom we talked in both Northboro and Centerboro, "vertical" communication—from generation to generation—is less full than "horizontal" communication, within the same generation. This bareness of communication with—and about—family members, particularly parents, may be related to the bareness of verbalization about the pastor. When the family, with whom the respondent has contact of high frequency (if not always of warm quality), is seen or talked about so barely, it is not surprising that the pastor, with whom contact is much more tenuous, is also described sparsely.

In Northboro we often received apathetic responses in what should be meaningful areas of concern in a person's private life—that is, family relationships, one's immediate and future situation, one's problems. Sometimes a feeling of futility was an inescapable inference. Many respondents seemed to reflect a way of life that was flat, despairing. This is particularly true of those who talked about drinking, loneliness, and marital difficulties as their more troubling problems.

Yet a correspondingly large number of respondents seemed to have realistic attitudes toward their lives, a positive rather than passive acceptance of a bad situation, with a feeling of hope that had no observable material basis but which was reflected in their religious attitudes and beliefs.

We must note, however, that the somewhat greater articulateness of the Centerboro respondents, who are of a higher socioeconomic level, may have given us an impression of false distinctions, while sentiments in the two localities may be less different than the manner of expression would indicate.

Religious Beliefs

In both Northboro and Centerboro we found warm, interested, and generally favorable feelings toward religion, the church, and the clergy, though some interviewees expressed their feelings on these matters no better and no more fully than they did concerning their family members. Responses in both communities indicate that the appeal of religion to the greatest number of informants is less meaningful as an intellectual discipline or as a philosophical orientation than as a source of satisfaction for deeper needs. The relation of the individual to his God seems to be more a matter of feeling and emotion than of opinion and speculation.

While true of responses in both communities, the foregoing is particularly applicable to Northboro. Here we found rather primitive, direct, simple statements about religious beliefs, with limited doctrinal explanation or elaboration. God is personal, accessible, a consoling and sustaining presence, someone to fall back on, someone to pray to for help. Many respondents expressed a strong belief in the after-life.

The Centerboro respondents think of God more as the Supreme Being and Creator. Though they believe God created life in general and human life in particular, their responses reflect a less personal relationship with God than do the Northboro respondents. And they express somewhat more sophisticated beliefs about the after-life, with considerable variety of personal interpretation. These distinctions may be related to the differences in socioeconomic and educational levels in the two communities. The greater variety expressed by the Centerboro respondents concerning their conception of the after-life may be related, to some extent, to the greater latitude often found in the beliefs of Protestants when compared with those of Roman Catholics (the majority of the Centerboro respondents being Protestant).

A striking finding from these interviews is the strong supportive trust in God expressed by our respondents in both communities. We felt that such feelings, if present, would be elicited by our questions as to what the world would be like without God, and what their lives would be like if they lost belief in God. These questions were asked also for a related reason—that is, we thought they would serve as checks against stereotyped, catechismic, or other routine doctrinal or impersonal answers regarding personal beliefs.

Almost without exception the concept of a world without God seemed intolerable to our respondents. A revealing distinction, however, is that in Northboro, the lower socioeconomic area, with lower educational level, God seemed to be a source of order, or of control in both social and individual life. He is guarantor of public and private morality, of humanness, and, of humaneness. In Centerboro, the higher socioeconomic area, God seems to provide meaning, purpose, and in some cases, beauty and guidance. Without God, it would appear, life in Northboro would be chaotic, without order; crime, selfishness, and persecution would run rampant. Life in Centerboro without God would be meaningless, purposeless, empty. The member of the lower socioeconomic group perceives God as controlling the hostile, destructive, and sexual impulses in others and in himself. With the loss of God, who is the primary symbol of his harsh, primitive, punitive superego, these impulses would no longer be held in check.

Almost without exception belief in God played a highly significant part in the world view of our respondents in both communities. God was seen either in personal terms as protective, compassionate, and accessible, or sometimes in somewhat more symbolic ways; but in nearly all instances the individual belief in God, the individual image and interpretation of relationship filled the need for security and relatedness. Whether God is seen as guaranteeing order and control, morality, and humaneness, as among our Northboro respondents, or, on the other hand, meaning, purpose, and beauty, as in Centerboro, the responses elicited by these questions have implications for mental health.

Dealing With Problems

In Northboro, one-third of the informants professed to have no problems. Another third talked about financial problems. The only other problems described with any frequency were physical illnesses and symptoms, and drinking. Several respondents referred to loneliness.

In Centerboro, over one-half of the respondents had experienced crises and problems in the areas of parent-child or husband-wife relationships, personal loss, feelings of depression, and the like. Though the Centerboro interviewees were of a higher socio-economic status, they also talked about economic and financial problems. There seems to be a tendency among the Northboro respondents either to repress or disguise their problems or to interpret those they do mention in physical and external terms. Just as ways of interpreting and identifying illness are closely related to ways of dealing with it, so this observed tendency toward anti-introspection would seem to be a factor that might influence the ways these people will deal with their problems.

A major impression we got in both cities is that people are

constantly coping with problems on their own. Human life is at best complicated, with constant problems of interpersonal and social adjustment. People seem to move "from crisis to crisis." Many have prayed when the going was rough. Though some are worried, some drinking too much, they are in the community; the fact that they are not in a hospital would seem to indicate that they are at least partially successful. In a series of brief interviews such as these, however, we cannot discern just how effectively they are coping with present problems. Nor do we know how much damage, as a by-product of coping, they may have done to others. In both communities the nature of some responses suggests that spouses and children may have taken a beating to enable some respondents to maintain, or to build, a capacity to cope.

The majority of the respondents in both towns indicated a certain degree of independence—that is, they want to cope with their own problems by themselves, whenever possible. In Centerboro, we could observe a greater readiness for making use of both religious and psychological resources for guidance. In Centerboro also we noted an awareness of the need for some kind of self-preparedness, whether through education or through vicarious experience, as a means of "softening" emotional blows, deprivations through loss in particular. This foresight is reflected also in the awareness of the need for training of intermediaries, auxiliaries to, or substitutes for, professional psychiatric personnel—such as law enforcement personnel, doctors, clergy, and teachers, in anticipation of various ways they could be of help at time of stress, from giving help personally to being effective in referral. This kind of foresight, either in regard to personal preparation through education or through experience— a kind of "inoculation"—or in regard to educating and training auxiliary or substitute mental health personnel, was less observable in Northboro. It may well be a product of higher education, of a planning or design-oriented way of life, and of longer-range goals.

In Northboro, we observed, the more frequent church attenders had gone to the clergy for help more frequently, and were more likely to go more frequently, than the nonattenders or the infrequent attenders. They seemed to be somewhat less likely to go to the clergy than the residents of Centerboro, of whom one-fifth or more had gone to the clergy for help, a considerably higher proportion than in Northboro. In contrast to the specific, problem-oriented reasons for the Northboro residents—jobs, alcoholism, children, spouses—the Centerboro residents tended to go for less clearly definable reasons, and to seek comfort and consolation.

In both communities considerable barriers stand between the people and the clergy as a source of help. In Northboro: lack of initiative to go, self-sufficiency, feeling that the problems were not important enough, and the fact that the clergy were not known well enough or were thought to have been unhelpful in some previous circumstance. In Centerboro: rapid turnover of clergy, the impression that the clergy are too busy, prayer as a substitute for outside help, type of sermons. In both communities, some degree of self-sufficiency seemed to constitute a barrier. The reasons people have for not going to see a clergyman may well be quite other than those they talk about, such as the apparent inaccessibility of the pastor, and may lie within the individual himself.

While people did not report much recourse to the clergy in time of trouble, interviews with members of the clergy in these same communities gave a somewhat different impression—namely, that they are fairly busy with counseling. Either they are busy, or they think they are, or, as could quite well be the case, other persons than those we happened to talk with go to them for counseling. From respondents among the clergy in Centerboro, we gained the impression that people come to them not only for such straightforward problems as where to get a job, and the like, but problems that have considerable emotional content—for example, regarding mixed marriage—and that require sensitivity and perceptiveness on the part of the counselor.

As we noted earlier, going for counseling to the clergy seemed to depend in large part on the personality of the individual clergyman; whether he is interested, warm, friendly, receptive, accessible. But this also seemed to depend as well on personality factors of the individual layman; for example, he may interpret as inaccessibility such unconscious things as his anxiety about the clergyman as a father-figure.

As for recourse to psychiatrists, past and future: In Northboro, none went and none would go. In Centerboro, none went, but some had indirect contact through the illness of a family member. Slightly less than half *would* go. Northboro respondents think of the psychiatrist's help as being advice-giving or "digging into one's past"; over one-third would not venture to say. Centerboro respondents had fairly clear ideas about what psychiatric help consists of, but limited information about resources.

High—sometimes insurmountable—barriers seem to block communication between psychiatrist and people in both Northboro and Centerboro. Northboro respondents are predominantly "against" psychiatry and psychology in general; they feel the psychiatrist has his own problems and therefore is not the best source of help in dealing with theirs; besides, they do not have the money. In Centerboro, even though the economic level is higher, most respondents talked about the cost of psychiatric help as a major deterrent, and expressed fear of what others would say as a factor in their reluctance to seek psychiatric help.

In both communities we found among the obstacles to securing psychiatric help: lack of money, reluctance to define oneself as mentally disturbed, and reluctance to undergo self-examination— that is, anti-introspection, a phenomenon that appears often as both a class factor and as a personality factor. But also the need to see oneself as independent, as self-sufficient, may work as an obstacle. There seems to be some evidence of a drive, an expectation of self-sufficiency, of ability to handle one's problems and periods of stress. This may be an individual matter, or it may be built into the culture. We see many examples in these two communities of how people fight through their own problems; to many, it never occurs to them to go for help. However, this independence may reinforce the hazardous pattern of "last-ditchism" which stands in the way of help on many levels, from cancer to mental disorder.

In comparing the responses from Northboro and Centerboro, we have emphasized the differences in socioeconomic and educational levels as important rational if not causative factors. However, when we consider readiness to go for help versus autonomy and self-sufficiency, personality factors may prove to be more important than socioeconomic factors. Why do some persons cope and others seek help? The degree of stress must be considered, but so must the question of what personality factors enter into determining whether the threshold is high or low. The nonclinical material we acquired from these interviews suggests that these personality differences may exist and that they may be dynamic and important. Trying to answer the question of the height and "crossability" of the threshold by reference *only* to socioeconomic class may be a gross oversimplification, for the answer may be much more subtle.

The laymen whom we interviewed in Northboro and Centerboro have told us some of their feelings about the clergy, as well as some of their religious beliefs, and about psychiatrists as well as some of their problems. They have thus given us a further perspective on the churches and mental health, as well as some impression of factors that facilitate or block accessibility to sources of help, religious or secular.

X

Self-Observation of the Clergy in Mental Health Endeavor

We have seen the efforts of the clergy in the area of mental illness and health from the perspective of patients in two mental hospitals and residents of two communities. Now we ask members of the professions most closely concerned their views—in this chapter, the clergy themselves, and in the following chapter, psychiatrists.

Here we shall report the responses of parish clergymen to questions which we asked them in a country-wide survey conducted by mail. We asked our respondents simply to tell us what they thought was the most important question we could ask about the church and mental health, and to give the reasons for their choice. In this way we prompted them to talk about issues that most closely concerned them in their own parish experience. They were later asked to answer the following five questions:

1. What aspects of your ministry (or rabbinate) do you consider most significant in contributing to the emotional and spiritual growth of the people you serve?

2. What are some of the obstacles that hinder your efforts to help the members of your congregation realize their potential for spiritual growth?

3. What do you consider the most difficult problem presented to you by a counselee? What action did you take in regard to this problem?

4. Can you suggest some practical techniques or procedures that you have found to be effective in counseling, and that might be of use to other clergymen?

[173]

5. What courses in theological school do you think have been of most value to you in your ministry? Are there any on which you now wish you had placed more emphasis?

In acquiring a panel of respondents, we first wrote to the directors or executive secretaries of each of the 212 State and city councils of churches in the United States. Each director was asked to send us names and addresses of ten to fifteen clergymen in his council, and to select clergymen with little as well as much experience in counseling, from rural as well as urban parishes, and representing a variety of denominations. One-hundred sixty sent the names requested. We then wrote to the second, sixth, and tenth clergyman on each list— a total of 480, of whom 166 replied. We contacted 45 Roman Catholic priests at a workshop on mental health. From names of rabbis selected from the membership lists of the rabbinical associations of the three major traditions (Orthodox, Conservative, and Reform) we received 80 replies.

In addition to the three major faiths, our respondents represent 14 Protestant denominations, as well as 24 States. We may assume that in spite of our request to the church council directors that they include clergymen with both little and much counseling experience, they tended to send us names of men who could give a good account of themselves. We may further assume that those clergymen who took the trouble to answer our mailed questions may be those most interested in, or troubled by, the issues of mental health. They would tend to be the clergymen most active in counseling parishioners or in community mental health activities. Thus we no doubt have a selection of respondents somewhat weighted toward the knowledgeable and the active. Also, by accident of our selection techniques, the respondents include the then president of the National Council of Churches and three other nationally known religious leaders. However, this enhances rather than invalidates our selection, since we have not sought a random cross-section from which to make statistical analyses and draw generalizations, but rather a variety and range of responses within which we may look for some common denominators.

In general, we will not enumerate certain types of responses, but rather we will integrate the information gathered from all these sources in such a way as to show some of the key issues of religion and mental health as the "working clergy" see them.

MOST IMPORTANT ASPECTS OF THE MINISTRY

Before presenting the personal responses from clergymen about their concerns in the mental health field, it will be well to place this discussion in a wider perspective. The clergymen were asked what they considered to be the most significant aspect of their ministry in contributing to the emotional and spiritual growth of their congregants. We did not give the respondents a list of items from which to choose; they were given complete freedom in answering the question. It is in the context of their responses to this question that further discussion of pastoral counseling should be set.

The choice of most significant aspects which occurred with greatest frequency was preaching, followed in close second place by counseling. Other choices in decreasing frequency were: pastoral visiting, worship, church fellowship, teaching, and the personality attributes of the clergyman.

The first and fourth choices, preaching and worship, concern what the pastor and the congregation do together in the church, in a "one-to-many" relationship. Counseling, visiting, and "fellowship" are concerned with what takes place outside the formal structure of the church, but within the religious community.

For the most frequent choice, *preaching,* responses ranged from strong defenses of simple Gospel preaching to considerations of the sermon as a means of clarifying needs and creating opportunities for spiritual growth. Some respondents expressed the belief that by way of practical, down-to-earth sermons the congregation, as a unit and as individuals, can develop both emotionally and spiritually. We found frequent emphasis on preaching as a basic Christian approach to life and as essential to the spiritual growth of the congregation. "This is our job," said one pastor; "this is the field in which we should excel. I deplore departures into preaching upon other subjects, or treating the sermon as an essay. To me it is interpretation of the Christian faith. Give a man understanding of his faith, and he can then be trusted to apply it to his own life."

Some who made preaching their first choice related it to problems of meaning and purpose and the realm of practical help, indicating ways in which sermons can point up needs that will lead to pastoral counseling.

Counseling is selected by the second largest number of clergymen as most effective in applying spiritual answers to their congregants' problems. While recognizing the place of sermons and rituals, some pastors find that nothing takes the place of the give and take of conversation with an individual or a group. It is only here, they feel, that the pastor can actually know and deal with the feelings of resistance and superstitions that stand in the way of emotional growth. "I try to make my sermons an emotional experience rather than simply a lecture, but even that has its limitations. Ritual may even more tend to re-enforce the resistances rather than being a new experience."

"Sermons have their place but they cannot do what individual contact can. The sermons of the prophets and of Jesus Christ himself bear witness to this. The fact that I in a measure can accept my humanity and understand myself is most helpful to others as they come to me for help with their emotional instability and immaturity."

Pastoral visiting is the third most frequent selection. Although many clergymen, and some social scientists, in talking about the "pastoral" role do not distinguish between counseling and pastoral visiting, most of our respondents have made this distinction. Some have seen opportunities for counseling relationships develop in the calling or visiting, others see the pastoral visit as an important aspect of their ministry in its own right.

In giving the reasons for his choice of pastoral calling, the pastor of a small church in the Northwest describes the way he has found to enhance personal relationships with his congregants through a kind of pastoral calling in reverse:

In addition to home visitation with the aged and lonely, my wife and I have three or four couples a week into the parsonage. Generally a candlelight dinner, interested and sympathetic conversation with them, and then perhaps cards. I realize this is most time-consuming—but it is a very natural and enjoyable experience. Problems of various sorts come out, theological questions are posed, et cetera.

And the rabbi of a conservative congregation in the Southwest draws upon his experience in working with hospital patients as well as home visitation, and with Christians as well as Jews:

The most fruitful area of my ministry is the pastoral one; particularly the hospital and home visitation. I have been able to reach a good number of individuals—both Jews and Christians as well as congregational and noncongregational members through this avenue. Without attempting to in any way "proselytize" or "grab people when they cannot get away," I have found that I can reinforce their spiritual and emotional lives through this avenue. Many of the Christian patients I have visited have grown stronger in their own faith and have achieved a more positive approach to Religion *per se*. In this area I try to function as a part of the supportive program with both patients and relatives.

Worship, fourth in frequency of choice by all respondents, is seen as the central religious act and as a focus of the religious life. Some pastors point out the significance of man's response to God's word, at the same time identifying emotional maturity as a secondary goal. Others see worship as bringing people into the presence of God, "strengthening faith in the Controller of the destiny of man."

Though church fellowship was selected fifth in order of frequency as the most significant aspect of the ministry, our respondents singled out many ways in which it can contribute to emotional and spiritual growth. Some identify church fellowship with small groups and group experience, considering the heart of the ministry to be in the relationships between persons. Those aspects in which people can be helped to find themselves, and move forward into rich interpersonal relationships, seem, to some respondents, to lie at the heart of the ministry; these go on in a small group and in individual counseling as significantly, if not more so, than they do in the traditional, formal, public forms of worship.

A southern clergyman, in explaining his choice of church fellowship, equates it with small-group experience, placing it in relation to worship, consultation, and the like in fostering emotional and spiritual growth. He considers that the primary role of the minister is

to guide and assist persons in developing a mature and adequate faith, including a reasonable world view and a basic understanding of the nature of man. Essentially, our study groups, family fellowships, organizational activities, church school and worship programs should contribute to this end. Small-group experiences and counseling opportunities are designed to meet more individual problems and to provide personal stimulus to emotional and spiritual growth. I personally feel that worship, the pulpit, the classroom, and personal consultation support each other toward this end.

Some respondents saw the personal attributes of the clergyman himself as of even more importance than any one aspect of his work. Replies ranged from such specific and readily identifiable qualities as kindliness and promptness, to the more elusive problem of the pastor's own mental health and its effect on his congregants.

The most significant factor in the mental health of congregants, some clergymen feel, is the mental health of the pastor. The best way he can help his people is to work for the improvement and stabilization of his own personality structure. Not only can he then be more effective in his ministry, they feel, but his own mental health serves as proof that his way of life is beneficial.

Some respondents who did not single out one specific aspect pointed to the manifold facets of the ministry, finding growth resulting at times from sermons, at other times from adult education classes, counseling sessions, or personal conversation in informal groups.

CLERGYMEN ASSESS THE ROLE OF RELIGION
IN MENTAL HEALTH

Closely related to clergymen's considerations of the most significant aspects of the ministry as they are related to emotional and spiritual growth are their sentiments about the relation of religion to mental health. Our respondents dealt with the role of the church, church personnel such as clergymen and other professional or volunteer religious workers, and aspects of religious faith itself in relation to mental health problems.

A Church of the Brethren pastor in Ohio believes that the role of religion in the healing ministry is for ministers to become "channels of the healing power of the Holy Spirit, and churches to provide a quiet place where the atmosphere of reverence and Holy Spirit will attract people who are in need."

Some respondents explored ways in which religious concepts and feelings rather than institutional factors might contribute to mental health. While some consider that our basic concept of God is the most important factor in determining whether our religion contributes to our mental health and general well-being, others ask whether the religious approach of the church in which the individual has grown up affords opportunity for growth, intellectually and emotionally, so that faith becomes an aid to maturing rather than an inhibiting viewpoint which must be constantly defended and protected. "In many years of counseling," writes a Baptist minister in Michigan, "I have found that individuals whose religion relates them to a continuous process of change and growth are invariably far happier and more secure than those whose religious ideas are tied into a brittle type of creed or mythology."

Some respondents referred to the disturbing effects of what they called "fear religion" and its possible contribution to mental illness. Not all religion is healthy, they believe. The fundamentalist type of religion of the most sectarian kind, with its emphasis on guilt and sin, may be related to mental illness. On the other hand the "happiness and positive thinking" cult has oversimplified the problem, and people may become more disturbed when they find that some easy formula does not produce an immediate solution.

Over two-thirds of the clergymen with whom we talked or corresponded had critical remarks to make concerning "fear religion." They deplored most a religion that inspired fanaticism and emotionalism, and almost invariably pointed to those who interpret the Bible literally as having these defects. They were especially critical of a religion of impossibly high ethical maxims, one which places an overemphasis on guilt and sin, creating a disparity between ideals of human conduct and realistic possibilities of attainment, and thus providing the kind of religious experience that may be a factor predisposing toward mental disorder.

The few members of extreme fundamentalist groups who responded in our study (perhaps most clergymen concerned with mental health and thus motivated to respond represented other traditions) tended to see lack of faith and lack of right relation with God as the predisposing factors in mental disorder.

THE CLERGY'S MOST PRESSING CONCERN

When the clergymen with whom we talked and corresponded were asked to identify the most crucial issue within the area of the church and mental health, the majority designated the specific problems of their parishioners as their primary concern.

A large number of responses dealt with inadequate home environments, family difficulties, and poor parent-child relationships. In regard to the last, the minister of a Congregational Christian Church in Kansas asks: "Is it insecurity which causes many parents to treat their children with such lack of respect? What religious and/or psychological insights would assist parents to feel more consistently toward their children?"

Another wide area of parishioner problems with which the clergy expressed concern is the whole domain of personality development. One minister graphically described these problems in the following way:

I can't quite respond with a specific situation which has been presented by a person. I can, however, say that the predominant numbers of people I see are having difficulty separating what we call the child of the past from the adult of the present. Most of them in their adult stages want so much to be rational, to set long-term goals, to do problem solving in line with the experience they have accrued. Yet, over and over again they have great difficulty separating the harsh, tyrannical demands of childhood from the adult goals. The patterns formed in early life have a tendency to carry over, particularly when it comes to religious relationships. Therefore, these people often see God in harsh, primitive terms. They have guilt feelings that are pathological; their anxiety revolves around impulses that seek to break through rather than around goal-directed behavior which would make them as good as they are. The only action to take in this regard is to try to help the person see what patterns he has used as he has developed himself, to stay with him long enough until he can understand both what he is and what he wants to be and then give him enough gentle love so that he can move in that direction. This takes time; it takes one who knows his own "child of the past"—and it takes a kind of relationship that doesn't grow up overnight.

Although our respondents seemed to recognize that there are important psychodynamic reasons for insecurities and other distress in their parishioners, most pastors felt strongly that one of the most important functions of religion is that it provides security. Yet some tend to give answers that take the shape of religious panaceas. An illustration of this comes from a minister on the West Coast: "It is lack of faith that is at the root of most people's psychological troubles. Sure, problems take many forms, but right-faith is the one solution that would cure the bulk of them." The conviction that spiritual living is integral to mental health is a theme that has been often reiterated by our respondents. Many laymen in our community studies made the same contention—that faith brings mental health— although they could seldom explain why they thought this was so.

Alcoholism is another problem which clergymen encounter frequently in their pastoral work. (Over four-fifths of the clergy whom we interviewed in a Midwestern community mentioned this as one of their most prevalent counseling problems.)

In emphasizing that the clergyman must be more than a referral agent for the alcoholic, one respondent singled out the pastor's willingness to get totally involved with the alcoholic on the slim chance that his concern might give the sufferer the strength to take new, careful strides. Otherwise, the victim is lost and the church must be reckoned among those who must take the blame for his aloneness.

In attempting to minister to a given parishioner and his problem in its entirety, the clergyman risks trespassing the boundaries of the social worker, possibly the psychiatrist, and even, if necessary, that of the parent. But regardless of the risk, he must be able to communicate his desire and his capacity to help. Here many crucial problems arise: they might well be termed "barriers to communication." The barriers seem to consist of the parishioner's attitudes toward the clergy and about mental health; but also they consist of the clergy's attitudes toward the people and about mental health.

BARRIERS TO COMMUNICATION

How many parishioners think of the church and the minister in terms of a demanding idealism and a harsh judgment, and how many as a source of understanding, comfort, and encouragement? Perhaps the greatest single barrier between pastor and layman is the latters' perception of the pastor primarily as an upholder of the moral law. This view of the minister as a moral arbiter can reduce the likelihood that he will be called upon as a source of help. A Rhode Island pastor reports:

I feel that one of the greatest obstacles that hinder my efforts is the mental image that my people have of the minister's role. The older members are reluctant to bring personal problems to me. I feel that they believe that it is the minister's role to sit in judgment. It is evident that this attitude is breaking down but I have only been here four years. Most of my counseling has been done with people that have come into the church during my ministry.

"The church at large has a faulty understanding of the task of the minister," says a Baptist minister in a Midwestern state. "Since the minister is regarded as a symbol of polite society and an organizer in the church, many people do not think to approach him for spiritual help."

Some of our respondents saw the problem of the social stigma that is still attached to mental illness in our society as an obstacle standing in the way not only of a pastor-parishioner helping relationship, but also as blocking recourse to other sources of help. One clergyman comments upon his experiences with this problem:

In mental illness of course we are consulted by the patient who has a sense of bewilderment, and also by the anxious relatives. Mental illness still seems to have a stigma in the minds of most people and here I think the denial of that with a religious imprimatur would help tremendously. People boast about an operation and solicit sympathy on that basis; yet they try so desperately to conceal mental illness.

Difficulties of communication are not solely attributable to parishioners' attitudes and perceptions. The clergy also may erect barriers to communication by some of their attitudes towards their parishioners, by their perception of the people to whom they minister. When asked what was the major obstacle to ministering to their people's emotional and spiritual needs, about 95 per cent of the clergy whom we queried found the obstacles to be in the parishioners—either in their deficiencies in spiritual or personality qualities, or in the cultural values to which they subscribed. About 5 per cent saw the obstacles in themselves.

The rector of an Episcopal church in Connecticut reflects sentiments shared by some other clergymen when he points to some implications of infrequent attendance:

Many persons attend church so infrequently that the actual influence of the church is very limited and can make almost no practical difference in the way they meet personal and family problems. Wider participation in the real purpose of the church in ministering to the community is needed. Many members still think of church work primarily in terms of church suppers and other similar activities.

A Presbyterian minister in Ohio is disturbed by his parishioners' apparent incapacity for personal growth:

Their lack of mental, emotional, and spiritual maturity makes it impossible for them to grasp the fundamentals of growth on a rational basis. They cannot reason through their predicament or problem with any facility, which makes it exceedingly difficult to establish the necessary foundation upon which to begin to help them.

A rabbi discerns the greatest obstacle as the spiritual disinterest on the part of many of his congregation.

Their obsession with materialistic values and hedonistic pursuits tends toward a grave disregard for the intrinsic values which religion per se offers. Too many of my people have forgotten the efficacy and the usage of prayer. The spiritual growth, consequently, is a rarity to so many in that their life values are diametrically opposed to the spiritual values of religion and its servant, the synagogue; further, people come too late for aid, and this places a high obstacle in the way of realization of their spiritual potentials. The modern stress on outwardness, on forms, on rites, on the attitude that religion has no bearing in life—except on the lock-tight compartment marked "religion." In sum total—the schizoid attitude in western civilization which separates religious values from life.

The few clergymen who saw the obstacles as inherent in *themselves,* rather than in their parishioners, called attention to the need for good communication, "which requires new frames of reference and a simpler vocabulary, which I have not mastered." They also pointed to such factors as "our uncertainty about our task, which makes us fail those who would turn to us." Some pastors admitted to a tendency to attempt too much, to spread oneself too thin. One pointed to the danger of the clergyman himself misunderstanding his congregation. "If the minister sees the *congregation* as obstacles to what he wants to do, he will react to them with hostility."

The pastor of a large community church in Ohio sums up the pattern of blockage of real communication by pointing to the misperceptions on the part of both the minister and the parishioner, and their reactions in accordance with them:

Obstacles that hinder our efforts to help the members really revolve more in the contractual agreement we have one with the other. Many laymen react in terms of how they perceive the minister, and the minister reacts in terms of how he perceives the congregation. But often, neither shares the perception which they hold about the other. For example, if the minister sees the congregation primarily as obstacles to what he wants to do, or feels they make impossible demands, then he tends to react to them in line with this whether he knows it consciously or not. The next obstacle is in the contract, and this has to be re-defined always. What are our expectations of the people, and what are their expectations of us? How are these in line with the primary task of the church to help the person know the self that's within him and relate that self then, of course, to the love of God?

We do not know whether the responses we received from the clergy accurately reflect the most serious impediments to their work. That was not the object of our inquiry. What is significant is that many clergymen single out the people's spiritual condition itself as the chief obstacle to dealing effectively with their parishioners. The very object of their professional concern is in a sense translated into a personal and emotional barrier between clergy and people.

CLERGYMEN'S CONCERN WITH THEIR COMPETENCE

Many clergymen reflected concern over their own adequacy to deal with parishioners' emotional conflicts and other related matters. Their self-criticism, and in some cases self-doubts, centered around two focal points: their own capacity and adequacy as persons, and their training and experience. The reservations about their own competence ranged from the lamentation that "in all my seminary training no one told me how many crackpots there would be in the ordinary church," to the fear that if the minister's training enabled him only to give temporary relief to people in trouble, basic underlying difficulties might be masked.

Some expressed doubts whether training for the pastoral tasks is really possible for a seminarian without any significant experience in parish work. A Baptist minister in Oregon replies that he has felt

quite inadequate for some of the situations which have developed in my ministry and [I] have thought seriously of taking a summer off to pursue some course of study to this end. I don't want to be a poor man's psychiatrist, but I can't help feeling that a summer could prove to be very beneficial. And there is little doubt that such a course would do me more good now than if I had taken it in seminary.

Although our respondents singled out deficiencies of training most often, many expressed concern about the wrong approaches which some clergymen, including themselves, make toward personal problems, approaches that they characterized as: the sentimental, which admits the problem but offers only platitudes; the obscurantist, which will not admit there is a problem; and the condemnatory, which assumes that emotional problems occur more or less exclusively among the "inferior" or the "sinful." Some wondered just what the minister can do in mental health matters and what he should not attempt. The responses ran the gamut from feelings of some competence in the area to feelings of great personal inadequacy. The positive side of the picture is presented by a Midwestern minister in a statement about his personal experience:

In my pastoral ministry of something more than thirty-five years, I find that the role of the minister in mental illness is largely supportive. In my experience a contact of even once a week has kept certain persons on a somewhat even keel so that they still operate with some success in society.

Another clergyman, however, is appalled at the general ignorance of his fellow ministers in his community in the field of psychology and the dynamics of human personality:

I don't see how they can do any effective counseling when they are involved in really important personality problems. I am convinced, too, that the kind of counseling most of our ministers do is very superficial to the fundamental problems of mental health. . . . And, although our boys are coming out of school better prepared than formerly, it is still amazing how few of them had any training in this area.

Some responses of those clergymen who had reservations about their own training and adequacy at least have a somewhat hopeful tone. They feel that the future will see possibilities to repair many inadequacies—on their own part through institutes, seminars, and training programs for men already in the clergy, and on the part of future clergymen through greater opportunities during their seminary training.

When asked to indicate what seminary courses they consider to have been most helpful in their parish ministry and which ones might have been given more emphasis, clergymen pointed most often to those in the area of psychology and counseling. Theology was the only other area mentioned frequently.

Many of the clergymen with whom we corresponded had specific suggestions on how to remedy the problem of pastoral incompetence, most suggesting revisions of curricula in theological schools. As one example, a New Jersey pastor writes:

I would suggest a course entitled: "The Minister and His Personal Contacts" which would deal with the various types of counseling the pastor has to do, such as premarital, predivorce, prefuneral, prechurch membership, prebaptismal, and "How to get there before it happens."

RECOGNIZING PARISHIONERS' PROBLEMS

One aspect of the problem of personal competence is the ability to recognize the problems of parishioners and to determine their degree of seriousness. How does one distinguish between the individual a minister can help and one who needs the services of a psychiatrist?

Whether a clergyman recognizes a problem and how he senses its degree of severity are questions that are intimately involved in the frame of reference or perspective he makes use of, consciously or unconsciously, for his evaluation. Among the clergy there seem to be two dominant frames of reference for looking at the same problem, namely, the theological and the psychological. There is a discernible trend toward combining these into a single frame of reference—what might be called a theo-psychological perspective. Among our respondents the large majority (two-thirds) could be described as employing an exclusively psychological perspective; somewhat less than one-third can be included in the theo-psychological, and only one-thirtieth in the exclusively theological.

Where a solely theological approach to understanding parishioners' counseling problems is employed, there may be considerable difficulty in making any of the clinical observations necessary for effective counseling. If guilt is understood only as the breaking of God's absolute commandments, rather than related to parental or societal inhibitions, the pastor can only suggest confession, repentance, and the like. If the guilt is pathological and compulsive, psychological insight is crucial to effect any change for the better. Similarly, if anxiety is related exclusively to "lack of faith" for the theologically oriented clergymen, the most logical step he would no doubt take is to encourage the congregant to have more faith. This is not only unlikely to be of therapeutic value, but in some circumstances can be harmful.

METHODS IN COUNSELING

When asked about procedures in dealing with congregants who come to them with troubles, clergymen did not limit their replies to descriptions of their methods. They had some questions of their own. What results have other ministers had in dealing with specific mental health problems, they asked. Have they found religion an effective agent in the care of mental disturbances? How serious is the danger of transference in the minister's counseling? What are the best means of breaking transference, if such is necessary? Can the minister and the psychiatrist together deal with guilt? Does the minister's counseling continue during his parishioner's psychiatric or other clinical treatment? If not, when does it stop, or resume?

Such questions as these reflect a readiness to call upon the psychiatrist and to find ways of working with him for the best interests of the parishioner. They also seem to reflect a certain degree of isolation, and a lack of communication not only with psychiatrists but also with other clergymen.

In discussing their counseling procedures our respondents described a multitude of approaches and techniques, based on their own experiences. A third of these are concerned with precounseling preparation and situations. Recommendations to learn the methods and insights of psychology were matched by suggestions to build confidence in the congregation. Several suggested that the pastor should make himself readily available, and publicize this availability. Some suggested setting up church counseling committees, as well as programs of group therapy.

We may divide the suggested procedures for dealing with the troubled parishioner in the counseling relationship into two aspects —attitudes (emotional and intellectual), and techniques. Suggestions for the most useful attitudes, as distinct from techniques, in counseling comprised a fifth of the total suggestions made. What we might distinguish as "emotional" attitudes included: be accepting, sympathetic, kind, unshockable, understanding. Give love, friendship. Be motivated. Suggestions for helpful "intellectual" attitudes included: be honest, objective. Use common sense. Remember that everyone is different. Be patient and unhurried.

Techniques employed in the counseling procedure itself can be described under two aspects, comparable to the two major orientations seen in assessing parishioners' problems: namely, psychological or interpersonal, and theological. (For simplicity, we might call them secular and religious.)

A fourth of the suggestions for techniques in the course of the actual counseling procedure could be described as theological. Some referred to simple theological resources available to the clergyman himself as he tries to be of help, such as: Pray. Have faith. Consult with the word of God. Have the spirit of the good shepherd.

Other suggestions in the theological category were suggestions for what to do with, or how to work with, the parishioner: Help him to have faith in Christ, and in Gods' love. Prescribe prayer, or spiritual and moral thoughts. Suggest (and have readily available) Bible readings and other religious literature.

The majority (three-fourths) of the suggestions for techniques can be described as psychological, or interpersonal. Some respondents recommended specific procedures: e.g., get a frame of reference. Keep him talking. Be a good listener. Learn to listen selectively. Ask careful questions. Also included were some "don't's": Don't give advice; don't pass moral judgments.

Some respondents emphasized general goals rather than specific procedures: Build confidence. Appeal to the best in your parishioner. Help him to visualize and realize ideals. Help him adopt a course of action.

Some recommended that the clergyman suggest solutions. Some seemed to combine the listening, supporting role, and the directing, suggesting role.

The practical procedures used by clergymen in counseling may be categorized in other ways than those we have already used. These are directive and nondirective methods, discussed in an earlier chapter. Though "directive" counseling is apparently not of high frequency among our respondents, clear references to it—or methods which are identifiable as such—were found in several responses. The rabbi of a temple in New Jersey suggests:

People in need come to a clergyman not for passive counseling, but for direct answers. A permissive attitude on the part of the clergyman does not square with the role of the clergyman as father. In such cases the counseling interview can be most inadequate and unsatisfactory to both parties.

Another rabbi states: "While generally a nondirective approach helps clarify the situation, people come to the clergy because they want direction. As a clergyman he has a specific role to fill."

Illustrations of what some clergymen mean by nondirective are the following:

It is difficult for the pastor to avoid passing moral judgment on the counselee. I have found that most people are aware of their moral lapse. Moreover, we should refrain from telling people what to do and think. Our approach should be that of an accepting listener who encourages his counselees to make their own decisions.

I would stress that one should be interested and sympathetic and should allow all the facts to come forward without making any explicit judgments. Only when all of the pertinent facts have been made clear can we then try to make an evaluation with our counselee. It should be the goal of the evaluation to elicit from him the necessary judgments pertinent to his problem.

Unless the situation is really critical, I find that the time taken to really make a friend of the counselee really pays off. Usually these situations in which they find themselves do not happen overnight and by the same token cannot be worked out to best advantage hurriedly. I try to take one step at a time with them, thus building up rapport and confidence.

I don't think any particular method is nearly so important as having love and understanding in your heart. If then we reverently approach them as human souls sitting beside us, and both in the presence of God, helpfulness is likely to result.

Some of these responses indicate that there is no sharp dividing line between directive and nondirective, nor even, perhaps, between theological and psychological counseling. One method clearly does not exclude the other. Rather than being arbitrarily described by mutually exclusive categories, such methods as these might more appropriately be designated as "supportive," or "responsive," or "empathic" counseling.

THE USE OF REFERRAL

In discussing counseling procedures, several respondents talked exclusively in terms of referral (about a tenth of all the suggestions had to do with ways of referral). Of these, most said that they made a standard practice of referring all parishioners with difficult problems to other sources of help. Others suggested discussing parishioners' problems with a psychiatrist and getting to know the community's resources. Several issued the familiar warning: Don't try to be a psychiatrist. These recommendations that referral be freely used lead us to further consideration of that topic.

The seemingly simple procedure of referring a parishioner to professional psychiatric care is compassed about with varied difficulties, including questions of location, and degree of development and competence of helping resources. Not the least of these is the image the clergyman may have of the psychiatrist, and vice versa.

In many communities, the clergyman and the general practitioner are the only reasonably near sources of help available. In one community with a population of 100,000, reports one observer, the nearest psychiatrist was ninety miles away. The nearest mental health clinic service was forty miles away and only ran two days a month. "It was there," he said, "that I had a very interesting conference with a clergyman, who discussed at great length the case load he was carrying. I couldn't help feeling that, practically speaking, here was a tremendous resource."

Even with facilities within reach, the problem is not always solved. A Fort Worth Episcopal rector poses the problem:

We are at a loss to evaluate psychiatrists. I am sure the experience varies with the geography but very few people want to put their loved ones in a state hospital but usually cannot afford the cost of a private sanitarium. Not infrequently the state hospital is better equipped than the sanitarium that resembles at times a modified jail.

One of the key issues in making a referral, as many an experienced pastoral counselor has learned, is the matter of "timing." The pastor can play an important part in bringing the disturbed person into relationship with spiritual and medical therapy. Because of his close relationship to his parishioners, he may be the first to detect symptoms of personality disorder. Where the pastor may need particular guidance, however, is in "timing," i.e., when to move into the situation and particularly when to make the proper referral to those professionally trained to deal with the specific disorder.

However, some warnings have been heard about haste and over-eagerness in referral. Father Noël Mailloux of the University of Montreal points out (1956) that it is especially important for the pastor to learn to make referrals in such a way as to avoid shock or personal criticism of the parishioner. He suggests such an approach to the parishioner as, "Well, you have a way of presenting things which is not the usual one. As far as I can see there may be something that is not quite right here and I am not sure I can handle it." Carefully opening the mentally disturbed person to doubt is nearly always a good means of leading up to eventual therapy. The time to refer may not be at the moment when the pastor decides the problem requires referral. Rather, a long supportive process, requiring great patience of the pastor, may precede actual referral. Father Mailloux warns that it is dangerous to be in a hurry, and that "it may take three months, five months, to make a referral. It doesn't matter. It's better to do it the right way and take your time."

Though psychiatrists report that a minor proportion of their patients come to them through referral by clergymen, there is clearly a need for a kind of "network" of professional or personal relationships within which a system of referrals could be developed. Such a system would give confidence to the clergy and others who are likely to meet varieties of problems which sometimes are outside their professional competence. A prerequisite for such relations is the development of better communication between clergymen and psychiatrists. Yet some pastors express concern about the degree of hostility on the part of psychiatrists for ministers or organized forms of religion, as well as the extent of hostility and suspicion on the part of clergymen toward psychiatrists. "We should be cooperating at a common task," says a pastor in Georgia, "but I think we ministers misunderstand the psychiatrists about as much as they misunderstand us."

This concern seems to be justified particularly when we hear the sentiments expressed by some clergymen in response to our request to compare the relative merits of religious and secular counseling.

A number of pastors expressed the view that it is only religious faith that gives a broad enough perspective to deal effectively with people who are in despair, anxiety, or personal tragedy. Psychotherapy, they claim, is basically only a system of techniques. It lacks the perspective, the depth of vision, the "cosmic orientation" that are needed to work effectively with people whose distress may be due to the disillusionment that comes about when achievements are at last seen to fall short of expectations, or when life seems to have lost its meaning, or when conflict or ambiguity of goals leads to a kind of blurring—even fragmentation—of identity.

Still others claimed that the religious counselor is a member of a community (the church) which will encourage and support the recovering client after sessions of counseling have ended. The secular therapist, on the other hand, can only hope that the environment to which the ex-patient returns will not cause a relapse.

Such sentiments as these among the clergy may or may not be valid in their own right. They may, however, in a general sense be barriers to good communication between the ministry and the mental health profession, and in a particular sense may impede the development of any effective and continuing referral process.

Father William Bier (1958), of Fordham University, has called attention to some of the wider implications of the problem of referral, pointing out that the roles of psychiatrists and clergymen differ, and that any obscuring of the difference would be disadvantageous. But, he adds:

it would be a mistake to assume that this is an attitude universally acknowledged among clergymen and psychiatrists. . . . Part of the difficulty that we are trying to work out and to move beyond arises from the fact that certain psychiatrists and certain clergymen have not observed the legitimate limits of their respective roles. . . . In very general terms, it would seem to me that we want clergymen to have at least an understanding of and respect for psychiatry and psychiatrists. More than this cannot be realistically expected of the average clergyman. . . . There is just as great a need to develop in psychiatrists an attitude of sympathy for religion, and an understanding of its role in the lives of their patients. Only when we have in both camps a sizable group which has this . . . basic understanding and willingness to work with the other group, only then, I think, are we going to achieve a substantial degree of collaboration between religion and psychiatry. . . . It has seemed to me for some time that clergymen are considerably more willing to learn about psychiatry than psychiatrists are to learn about religion. . . . It is the fear of not finding this kind of over-all sympathetic treatment of religion which has prevented many a clergyman from making a psychiatric referral even when he felt psychiatric help was needed.

The fear of finding an unsympathetic attitude toward religion is related to the fear expressed by some clergymen that the psychiatrist will "rob" the parishioner of his religion, that getting well may involve becoming irreligious. The shift in identity from parishioner to patient seems to imply a nonreligious though healed patient who may never again be a parishioner.

Coupled with a concern that the psychiatrist may merely help the patient "adjust" rather than help him relate to more universal goals and that in the process the parishioner as patient may "lose his religion," may be a certain degree of anxiety on the part of the clergyman about his own loss of role. In his attempt to help the individual parishioner, usually in a counseling relationship, the pastor may be reaching for a redefinition of one aspect of his ministry that will impart more significance to his total role, his total ministry. When he refers a parishioner, he acts as an intermediary rather than as a mediator, as a "middle-man" rather than as an "end-man." He may, at heart, be reluctant to "surrender" the parishioner to someone who then begins to communicate with him at a level of greater depth and significance than the pastor had been able to reach.

SUMMARY

When we asked members of the clergy to examine aspects of their ministry pertinent to mental health, we tried to avoid the specific confines of pastoral counseling itself. Some respondents expressed concern with the broad question of the role of the individual's religious beliefs and orientation as a factor in mental health, seeing the individual's personal concept of God primarily as determining whether religion will have positive or negative effects in regard to mental health. (Several clergymen qualified their responses by pointing out that mental health is less a goal of religion than a by-product.) If the church, if religion, relates the individual to processes of growth and change, it is more likely to have positive effects. If, on the contrary, religion emphasizes guilt, sin, an inflexible kind of creed, and unrealistic moral and ethical ideals, it may have negative effects.

Most respondents focused upon the things that they had found to be most critical to them in their ministries and most demanding on their capacities. These were the problems faced by their parishioners, and their own role in helping them deal more realistically and effectively with them. Many were deeply concerned with their own limitations in attempting to deal with individuals in distress.

Yet only two pastors referred to the danger that providing relief through religious counseling might cover up deeper-lying difficulties that require psychiatric intervention. Not only can comfort prove to be a hazardous substitute for therapy, but religious counseling, in spite of its claims to wider, deeper, more universal orientations, runs the risk of seeming to bring about a resolution while the conflict remains essentially untouched at a more obscure level of the personality.

A major concern seemed to be the difficulty of reconciling the clergyman's traditional role qua clergyman with that of a psychologically astute resource for individuals facing baffling conflicts, relationships, decisions; how, in short, to bring the two fields of religion and psychology to an effective amalgam in the person and function of the clergyman.

From our survey a picture emerges not of clergymen with serene confidence in religion, in the church, in themselves when confronted with mental health problems, but rather of men in a dilemma: considerable ambivalence about the efficacy of religious resources, and at the same time reservations and anxiety about referring parishioners to psychiatrists and other professional resources. Serious barriers to communication, to understanding, to perception seem to exist between clergyman and psychiatrist, between clergyman and parishioner, and often between clergyman and clergyman.

Since the relationships between clergymen and psychiatrists, which seem to come to a focus in the matter of referral, are a matter of some concern to us, we interviewed a cross-section of psychiatrists in a large eastern city in order to learn something of their perception of the clergy, and their impressions of what the church is doing, and what it might do, in the area of mental health. In the following chapter we will present their views as they look at religion and the clergy vis-a-vis mental health.

Some of these psychiatrists have had no or little contact with members of the clergy. Others speak from personal contact with clergymen who may have been their pastors, their patients, or their associates in such mental health matters as interdisciplinary conferences or dealing with patient-parishioners.

XI

Psychiatrists View the Clergy

In their writings and formal statements, psychiatrists, like anyone else, measure their words and weigh their opinions. We wanted to learn what form their opinions might take in a more private discussion. What other and fuller sentiments may have been held back? What qualifications might be added, what subtracted?

Having read much of the literature containing the more or less formal statements of psychiatrists on the topics of the clergy, pastoral counseling, and the implications of religion for mental health, we too were faced with these questions. In an effort to "get a feeling for" the possible answers, we interviewed 24 psychiatrists in private practice in a large metropolitan area, selecting every sixth name from the alphabetical listing for the area in the membership list of the American Psychiatric Association (1957). The questions were as follows:

1. In what percentage of your patients do you find clear-cut religious themes in the content of the patient's illness?

2. What percentage of your patients have been sent you by the clergy?

3. The clergy often ask when they should refer parishioners to psychiatrists. What would you suggest?

4. Do you ever utilize the clergy in any way in the treatment process?

5. As you may know, for every psychiatrist in the country there are about 35 clergymen. Do you think that these clergymen might be a useful resource in combatting mental illness? What do you

Material for this chapter was prepared by John Dickinson.

think is the most effective thing they could do for the mental health of their parishioners?

6. Can you tell me something, briefly, about your own religious position.

The questions were asked as open-end questions and, within limits, fullness of response was encouraged. All our respondents were, of course, assured of anonymity. The interviews ranged in length from thirty to fifty minutes.

Although we begin with a presentation of the attitudes toward religion of our subjects, these attitudes were elicited by the *last* question on the questionnaire, as well as in the short period of informal conversation which usually followed the end of the interview proper. We asked this question last in the belief that, as a highly personal subject, it could better be introduced after the rest of the questions had been dealt with. We discuss this question at this point because the responses to it constitute a frame of reference for the remaining questions.

Over half of our respondents say that they are not religious in any formal way or that they feel no need for religion or are atheists or wouldn't care to say, or make other comments of like content.

Some replies of those who say they are not religious in any formal way are the following:

Well, I have no religious beliefs in the ordinary sense. . . . I have no religious affiliations.

In a formal way, I am not very religious, but I have respect for my own faith [the respondent is Jewish]. This is true of all my immediate family. I don't take it literally. I have been greatly influenced in my religion by my parents, except that they were too strict. . . .

I started out in a little town in North Carolina as a Methodist. I still technically belong to the church I entered when I was thirteen years old, but I no longer have any truck with it, don't know what it stands for, and seemingly disagree with it. I do not like those aspects of formal, organized religion which call for exclusiveness.

I value good works higher than faith, but I also place a high premium on faith. I don't have the foggiest notion of what God is, no basis for adequate judgment. . . .

A similar lack of strong affect is seen in the responses which we classified as *feel no need for religion:*

I don't feel any need for religious affiliation. . . . I guess that is what you want; though it might be a matter of how you define religion.

I have been in childhood an Episcopalian. Since college I have attended no church . . . can't say I have no religion . . . but I'm not one who personally wants close association with a church.

The more outspoken of the two atheistic respondents also says in the somewhat cautious beginning of his response, "I have myself no religious inclinations." The other simply gives the terse reply, "Atheistic."

Four respondents report a definite commitment to some religious institution, though one of these, saying that he is a baptized Lutheran, precedes this assertion with the remark, "I have no religious position."

Many of these informants have what might be called a benevolently instrumental view of religion: they respect it and value it as a means of strengthening their patients' egos, furnishing them identities, and giving them direction:

I've been impressed with the values of continuing cultural affiliations. . . . I'm thinking of a Jewish patient who, despite the difficulties he's had, is proud of his tradition. . . .

It's a question of identification. . . . religion is like rock and roll. . . .

Religion can be an integrating force within a person's life.

. . . patients find strength in their belief. . . . I encourage it.

They believe in the good of the church, but with only two or three exceptions, seem not to value church attendance or affiliation for themselves:

I don't belong to any church, but I believe in the good of the church.

Still, having gone through an orthodox Freudian analysis, I've ended up with the conclusion that the church is the major bulwark against man's inhumanity to man . . . maybe education is just as important.

The focus has to be on the importance that the patient attaches to his own religious position and the help that the patient's religion has been to him, whatever his belief is.

It is hard to escape the impression that the response, "I'm not religious in any formal sense," is a kind of fence straddling. However, two men expanded on this in such a manner as to give it a content which was otherwise missing: belief in the perfectability of man, feelings of awe, and the capacity to be moved by human tragedy and human grandeur.

Some people have at various times found it not at all impossible to arrive at the conclusion that there is no conscious personifiable power outside of man which will intervene, upon appeal, in man's affairs. Nevertheless, it is well known that most people believe in such a power, even to the point where expressed disbelief becomes offensive and threatening to them. The disbeliever who wants to maintain his intellectual honesty is faced with two alternatives: to express his disbelief and take whatever consequences this may entail; or, by exploiting the fact that there is much that we do not know, both in the realm of external reality and of the human consciousness, to "vagueify" his conceptions in such a way that he can still conscientiously use a religious terminology. For example, the respondent who hadn't "the foggiest notion of what God is" had previously remarked, "I like all [aspects of religion] which emphasize . . . respect for a Supreme Being." Thus, intellectual respectability is maintained, and the only price is an occasional absence of basic communication.

For the psychiatrist, and often for his patients, the immediate gain is appreciable. Recognizing religion as an existential reality, and saved from conflict by his own commitment, he can, as we will see in the responses in these interviews, utilize both religion and the clergy in total dealing with patients, harbor encouraging hopes for the cooperation between religion and psychiatry, and welcome the clergyman as an ally in the struggle against mental illness.

With this discussion of the personal religious positions of our psychiatrists providing a backdrop, we can turn to the remaining questions with the feeling that the stage has been set for them. They give a picture of the kinds of responses we might expect to obtain from a more extensive inquiry—rationalization and analysis from men who are trained to be rational and analytical, absence of impassioned commitment, and a generalized appreciation of the positive contributions of religion to mental health by men who are in a position to see these contributions and can use their appreciation of them as an adaptation to the wide diffusion of pro-religious sentiment in American society.

When we asked, "In what percentage of your patients do you find clear-cut religious themes in the content of the patient's illness?" the most frequent responses were "very little" or "very few," "less than 5 per cent," and "5 to 10 per cent." When we asked our respondents to identify some of these religious themes, the most frequent appeared to be "problems of conscience, right and wrong" and "utilization of religious concepts in irrational guilt." Two respondents qualified their estimate in the following ways: "Religion as concern with right and wrong . . . this is what people come to psychiatrists for. To learn to deal with guilt." "Religious people have problems of conscience, but most people today are not having problems of conscience . . . less than 5 per cent."

Schizophrenics in particular and psychotics in general were mentioned by six men as often showing specific religious content. Since most of these psychiatrists were in private practice, they saw few psychotic patients. The one exception was on the staff of a private mental hospital. His response to the first question is worth quoting for its bearing on the subject of religious content in psychotics:

"I've been poring that one over . . . 5 to 10 per cent . . . it's a little hard to judge . . . very often there is something religious that's not in conflict. There was this woman in a catatonic episode. She leaned very heavily on Christian Science, but I think that that was just something to lean on . . . then there's the delusional type, which looks at the sun for several hours because God is up there. . . ." [Which of these two types is the more frequent?] Oh, the delusional type, by two or three to one.

Either spontaneously, or as response to auxiliary questioning, several of the psychiatrists commented on the question of how basic religion was to the problems of these patients in the content of whose illness it appeared. The comments have intrinsic interest in themselves:

[*Did religion enter into their difficulties?*] No, religion was just an important part of their lives.

[*What is the relationship of religion to their problem?*] Well, I'm thinking of two patients where this is quite important . . . both had turned to their minister. . . . It is difficult in all these cases to separate the personal problems and the religious themes; they become so interwoven.

I feel that very few people have a religiously significant life and, therefore, would not have religious themes connected with their problems. Conventional, formal, ritualized religion sometimes promotes regression to the patient's five year old conscience. [*Does religion affect the five year old conscience?*] The five year old conscience is not affected by religion, though it may be affected by the minister. [*What about the effect of the parents' religion on the five year old conscience?*] No, except as it reflects deeper feelings. [*How basic do you think it is in such cases?*] Don't know . . . can't generalize . . . the girl who thinks she is the Holy Virgin and has had an immaculate conception. . . . I am liable to see religion as one of a set of (causational) factors. I have seen a few people puzzled over some religious theme, but not very many are disturbed over these issues.

Summarizing the responses to Question 1: Our respondents do not see many patients who exhibit explicit religious themes in the content of their illness. There is some indication that religion in a more general and less traditional sense, interpreted by them as conflicts of conscience or as concern about right and wrong, makes a more frequent appearance. Religious content is said to be more frequent among psychotics than among neurotics. Where elicited, ideas about how basic a part religion plays when it does appear vary, though there is some consensus that it is used as a rationalization or vehicle for more fundamental problems.

These psychiatrists take a rather narrow interpretation of religious themes, although this interpretation may have been evoked by our wording of the question (i.e., "clear-cut").

According to the experiences reported by our respondents, referrals to them by clergymen are rare, nearly one-half reporting none. Three added that they had clergymen as patients. One psychiatrist replied: "A lot of cases have been referred to me by clergymen, partly perhaps because I am on the social service mission of my church; about 15 to 20 per cent of the total cases I see are referrals from the clergy."

When asked when they suggest the clergy should refer parishioners to psychiatrists, our respondents gave as the most frequently appearing component of responses to this question one which may be paraphrased variously as when the parishioner appears sick, when he exhibits danger signals, or when he shows obviously bizarre and/or psychotic behavior.

Other frequent responses were: when there has been no progress in counseling; when the clergyman becomes too involved, feels out of his depth or uncomfortable with a parishioner.

A further group of responses can best be described by the responses themselves:

When the apparent religious problem is part of a mental illness.

Well, this is a very complex matter, yet over the years I have found some clergymen, Catholic priests, who spotted overly great need to confess and recognized that this went beyond ordinary religious ritual.

When religion is being used by the patient in a destructive way.

Because of the importance of this question in the context of the present study and our attention in other chapters to the problem of referral, we will here present in full those three responses which seem most comprehensive.

From respondent A:

I would suggest the following (but not in order of their importance):

1. The parishioner who comes to the clergyman without really strong religious feelings; when the minister feels he is getting nowhere with them, he should refer them to a psychiatrist (especially true for a man with little or no psychiatric training).

2. The person who comes with a religiously phrased problem and has a strong emotional bias, so that the patient cannot lay hold of his problem with any real objectivity and cannot, therefore, use the religious resources creatively should be referred.

3. Any person who comes for counseling and "knows" but cannot accept

the emotional feelings involved in his problem or its answer should be referred; he is only able to intellectualize.

4. Whenever there is a barrier between the clergyman and his counselee and/or he does not seem to get anywhere, he should refer the person.

From respondent B:

It is difficult to give a simple answer; they should refer:

1. The obviously sick person (psychotic).

2. Anyone with distortion in perception or feeling; such a patient has only a tenuous relationship with reality in such cases. I feel clergy can sometimes do harm by not referring such people as involutional depressives (usually women), and paranoids; they require skilled help.

3. Cases involving familial relationships (husband-wife or parent-child) that do not seem to yield to efforts by clergy; at least a consultative relationship with a psychiatrist should be established.

4. Anxiety neuroses unrelated to reality (usually deep-seated and dealing with the unknown); can be depressions or compulsive states.

From respondent C:

Clergy should refer:

1. An obvious psychotic problem; should be referred at the point when the minister recognizes it for what it is.

2. When the clergyman gets too involved and refers out of anxiety and his own involvement.

3. When the clergyman begins to lose his own role and becomes a psychiatrist (unless that is what he wants to become, depending on how he sees his own role).

4. When the minister cannot meet the need because of time limitations, energy limitations or other demands (family, personal, etc.).

When asked if they ever utilize the clergy in any way in the treatment process, half of our respondents gave a definite "Yes" to this question; only three gave a definite "No." A quarter indicated that they do so occasionally, and they speak favorably of the idea.

A cross comparison of these responses with those to Question 2, which asks about what might be called the reciprocation of the clergy in this regard (*What percentage of your patients have been sent you by the clergy?*), as well as with the responses to Question 6 (regarding the psychiatrist's own religious position), would appear to rule out attitudinal factors as the basis of the reciprocal referral relationship we have described and would lend weight to interpreting it in terms of the "contacts" mentioned in connection with Question 2. Where such contacts exist, we may hypothesize, they result in reciprocal referral. Where they do not exist, there tends to be no referral in either direction.

One respondent brought up the question of social class differences in the religiosity of patients. In response to Question 4: "Yes. Sure. Quite frequently with Catholic patients . . . mainly in the Urban General Hospital out-patient clinic. . . . I advise them to take up the matter with their priest . . . very rarely otherwise."

And in response to Question 1: "The percentage is 'very low' . . . this happens to be because I deal with somewhat sophisticated people who have little formal religion."

In view of the high cost of psychiatric treatment and the evidence which has been adduced in other studies for the upper social class status of patients in private treatment, these statements ring true. Yet a complex question arises out of this situation: If clergymen do become a more effective mental health resource, if they learn how to refer effectively, they will presumably do so without regard to social class; and who will pay the psychiatrist?

The most frequent response to the question, Do you think that these clergymen (35 for every one psychiatrist) might be a useful resource in combating mental illness?, was an unqualified Yes (one-half of the respondents). The qualification most often added can be paraphrased as: if they have the proper training and/or experience. Another qualification assumes the form of a general hortatory statement: The clergy and psychiatrists should work together. Only three men said "No," but one respondent said, "We need fewer clergy and more psychiatrists." He himself was an Episcopalian and had one of the largest percentages of referrals from the clergy. Perhaps he simply meant what he said and implied no invidious distinctions.

It may be that the overwhelmingly affirmative response to this question is explained by the one man who said, "A wise person may be presumed to be a useful resource in combating mental illness." And then added, "My personal conviction is that psychiatrists will never 'treat' more than a tiny proportion of those who might be considered to suffer from mental illness. Most such persons will be 'treated,' if at all, by teachers, clergy, and the like."

Of the three most frequent responses to the question, "What do you think is the most effective thing they (the clergy) could do for the mental health of their parishioners?," two recommended activities which clergymen already like to think of themselves as performing well. These are, *concentrate on the spiritual welfare of the parishioners:* "I am old fashioned enough to feel that the minister should concentrate on the spiritual welfare of his people; if he is really good, he can help them. He does not need to be a psychiatrist. People need spiritual help—a direction in life. . . ." and *listen skillfully:* "They should learn to listen skillfully. I'm sure there are many who do it already. . . ."

The most frequent of these three response-elements is the recommendation that clergymen should come to *understand their own limitations and functions:*

Somehow, he should stress his nonofficial capacity, he should show the parishioners his humanity, including what is wrong with him. And he should let them show him their humanity.

Something should be done about the motivation and selection of the men who enter the ministry. So many are really sick and very confused. They choose the vocation for their neurotic motives, and this comes close to the essence of the problem.

In regard to the recurring response-element *emphasize or develop pastoral counseling or pastoral aspects,* nearly all our respondents rate the pastoral function of the clergy high on the list of those things which the clergy can do for the mental health of the parishioners.

If we classify all response-elements by the criteria: refers to a one-to-one relationship; refers to a one-to-many (minister-congregation) relationship; and refers to mixture or reference indeterminate, we find that the one-to-one items outnumber the one-to-many items by more than twenty to one, and outnumber the mixed reference items by about three to one. The only clearly one-to-many item occurred as "Talk about it (mental health) in their sermons."

Coming from a group of psychiatrists, this kind of reaction is hardly surprising. What is surprising is the almost total absence of any emphasis on the possible ways in which the clergyman, as one who regularly faces a fairly large group of people and who has a multiplicity of relationships with small and large groups, might use such relationships in an educative or even group therapeutic manner.

Even the response-elements we have classified as "mixed"—items such as "give a sense of belonging," "serve as good models," and "concentrate on spiritual welfare of parishioners"—seem more heavily weighted with the one-to-one emphasis than with the *one-to-many*. Yet the pastor is one who "tends a flock"!

In sum, the psychiatrists with whom we talked point to the emphasis on the one-to-one relationship and a concentration on the traditional functions of the clergy, refined and made more effective by training, by greater interaction with psychiatrists, and by more acute self-awareness. On the whole there seems to be an uninhibited recognition of the importance of the clergyman's role in mental health combined with criticism directed at the way this role has been played in the past and a lesser degree of criticism directed at the way it is still being played. None is opposed to religion, none expresses the idea that the religious view of reality as such may create problems for his patients, and all welcome the assistance and support that religious affiliations provide for their patients.

PART THREE

Summary

XII

Religion and Mental Health: Demographic and Personal Variables

Our summary is in two parts. In this chapter we summarize some of the implications for mental health of such readily ascertainable factors in religion as church membership, attendance, and similar demographic and personal factors.

In the following and final chapter we propose areas of emphasis in which the churches can strengthen their contributions to mental health.

When we consider the relation of religion to mental health or mental illness, we must not only define the related variables but we need to find some tangible ways to describe the religious phenomenon, whether as an activity, as a value, or as a social or individual matter. In this study we have simplified the problem somewhat by working on a more or less descriptive level. Now we select some specific religious factors on both a descriptive and a functional level, and attempt to relate them to selected mental health variables.

Several indices have become traditional, particularly when studying religion from a sociocultural perspective. One such index is church membership. While membership is usually seen in a broad descriptive or statistical context, it can sometimes be observed from the viewpoint of the individual. We can ask what is the quantitative description of membership in a given community or at a given time, and what are some of the qualitative implications, for that community or time, of much or little membership, of increasing or de-

Material for this chapter was prepared by Dr. Nathan Altshuler.

creasing membership. We can also ask what membership means to the individual member. Facts about membership, of course, disclose little about the religious beliefs of individuals, their religious orientation, or the significance of religion in their lives—or even about their religious practice and behavior.

A somewhat more descriptive index is frequency of attendance. This also has both sociocultural and personal implications, though it, like membership, remains predominantly on a quantitative, descriptive level.

Contributions to the church and other religious work may reflect degrees of religious concern. In 1956, for example, 50 Protestant and Eastern Orthodox church bodies reported contributions totaling $1,842,592,260, a substantial increase over the previous year. The average annual contribution per member for forty denominations was $53.94. (The highest average for any denomination—$194.12 per member—was reported by the Seventh Day Adventist Church.) While the amount of contributions may reflect broad trends, from rising building costs to the strength of a denomination, and may be one measurable indication of personal interest, it still tells little about the religion of the people.

Attitudes and sentiments towards religion, while a frequent objective of study, do not reflect such aspects of religion as the individual's religious orientation, since agnostic, humanistic, and other respondents who are nonreligious in the traditional sense may yet express positive sentiments toward religion.

Frequency of prayer comes closer to revealing the meaning of religion for the individual; but before it can begin to tell much of real significance, sheer frequency must be related to other aspects of prayer such as content and object (e.g., petition or thanksgiving) and to other aspects of religion.

Religious beliefs also have been the object of many sociological and sociopsychological studies. Yet the categories are often crude—e.g., "Do you believe in God? Yes or No."—and the findings misleading.

Anticipating some of the weaknesses and possibilities for misunderstanding inherent in these indices of religion, we will relate three of them—membership, attendance, and prayer—to certain aspects of mental health and to some other selected variables.

How many persons say they are religious? A test sampling of the population in March, 1957, in a "trial run" by the U.S. Census Bureau, included a question about religion (although the question was eliminated in the 1960 census). Ninety-six per cent of those interviewed reported they professed a religious devotion, 3 per cent said they had none, and 1 per cent gave no answer. (The exact meaning of "a religious devotion" was not explained in the report.) In 1952 a Gallup poll found 97 per cent of the people sampled believed in God. A nationwide survey conducted for the Joint Commission by Gerald Gurin, Joseph Veroff, and Sheila Feld (1960), shows that 97.5 per cent of the persons interviewed gave a religious preference. (This high percentage reflects inclusion of some answers indicating affiliation with religious groups without indicating a religious commitment.)

A discussion of the relevance of selected religious factors for mental health must be considered in the light of such findings as these. With "religion" so prevalent, it is difficult to say what should or should not be attributed to it. When nearly the whole population claims to be religious, the answer obtained to the question concerning religion's relevance for health depends not only upon what one considers to be religion, but also on what one defines as indices of health.

A comparison of religion and health in the United States and other countries would, of course, be a problem of astronomical difficulty. With the variety of values displayed by disparate cultures, and the differing concepts of health and illness, attempts to measure health across cultural boundaries is a thousandfold more difficult than within the United States. And the complications would not be limited to the health indices, but would extend to religion as well. Denmark, for example, has higher suicide rate than the United States. Yet, though we should learn that the Danes, like ourselves, were 97 per cent religious, we could not say whether they were healthier or not, unless we were ready to say that suicide was unhealthier than homicide or vice versa.

Are the 2 or 3 per cent of the persons in the United States who do not claim religion the people who are emotionally ill? If they are, they are not the only persons in distress. While the actual prevalence of mental disorder in the population at large is not known, various studies on limited populations do provide some indices. The studies surveyed by Richard J. Plunkett and John E. Gordon (1960) show a mental disorder prevalence ranging from 1.6 per cent to 33 per cent of the individual populations studied. In the survey by Gurin *et al,* (1960), almost 20 per cent of the persons interviewed answered *yes* to the question: Have you ever felt that you were going to have a nervous breakdown? If we assume the statistics for health are as reliable as those for religion, we must infer that the prevalence of emotional disorder is, at its upper limits, ten times greater than the prevalence of nonreligion. Thus, there must be persons in the United States who exhibit both emotional illness and religious devotion.

But perhaps the 97 per cent who claim religious devotion are not equally religious and inquiry might show that the more religious are actually healthier than the less religious. Here we confront an almost unanswerable question as to who is more religious and who less so, as well as what we mean by "religious." The variety of ways of expressing religious concern are great and the beliefs of any one individual complex. Not all would subscribe to the view that regular church attendance is the central feature of religious expression. But neither would all agree that concern for fellow human beings, alone, is sufficient basis to call one's self religious. In this chapter we shall consider overt expressions of religion that allow of some measurement; some measures conceived by us and some by other researchers in the field.

The question has been asked, and answered variously, as to whether there is a religious resurgence in the country at present. The first facts available are the trends in church membership and church attendance. In 1950, 57 per cent of the total population were reported to be church members. By 1956, the figure for church membership had risen to 62 per cent of the total population. Figures for attendance show an even more striking change. In April 1950, 39 per cent of the adults interviewed by the American Institute of Public Opinion stated they had attended church the preceding week; in April 1957, a poll revealed that the figure had risen to 51 per cent. The annual value of new construction of religious buildings rose from 409 million dollars in 1950 to 775 million in 1956.

Was the country more religious at the end of these seven years? Are these adequate religious indices? Was the country healthier? Again, what should we use as health indices? Divorces declined a fraction but so did marriages. School enrollment showed an appreciable increase. The stock market hit new highs during one of the steepest rises in its history. On the other side of the picture, the Federal Bureau of Investigation Crime Reports show a 13.3 per cent increase in major crimes from 1955 to 1956. The rate of increase in crime for the six-year period from 1950 to 1956 was four times as great as the rate of population growth. Facts we need most are, here again, lacking: the prevalence of mental disorder in the population for 1950 and for 1956. The number of first admissions to mental hospitals increased and so did the number of patients returned to the community. But hospital admissions are not a good index; more persons receiving care and treatment due to increased facilities or increased knowledge of available facilities cannot be used as a statistic to show increased mental illness. With such a complicated picture, it would be hazardous to attempt to portray the role of religion.

CHURCH MEMBERSHIP RELATED TO SELECTED INDICES OF SOCIAL HEALTH

Several studies have attempted to determine the effect of church membership upon the social health of the community. The following studies asked that order of question for particular communities within the United States.

Thorndike (1939) tried to determine what makes a city a good place to live. His index of "goodness" (which we might call social health) was based upon 37 separate factors, including such items as infant mortality, incidence of extreme poverty, per capita deaths from automobile accidents, percentage of young persons in school, and percentage of illiterates. He then proceeded to correlate the "goodness" scores of the cities with a number of separate variables, among these being the proportion of the population who were church members. His findings revealed that total church membership per capita had no significant correlation with the goodness score. (Indeed, for a sample of 295 cities he found a negative correlation of —.22, slightly above the level of significance.)

Thorndike (1939) sums up his section on religion with the observation that the communities with the largest percentage of church members

are below average in good reading, home ownership, and continuance in school, and have more than their share of illiterates and child labor.

To offset these damaging affiliations, we find that church membership is antagonistic to homicide, deaths from venereal diseases, and illegitimate births. . . . Church membership is thus still affiliated with typical features of traditional morality, if not with the broader aspects of welfare.

On the whole, unless the better communities under-report their church membership or the worse communities over-report theirs, we must suspect that the churches are clubs of estimable people and maintainers of traditional rites and ceremonies rather than powerful forces for human betterment.

Why should noble men and women give their time and money to make the church great and strong if communities where it is strong are no better than those where it is weak? What are the churches doing with their prestige and power if they are neither helping the health and education and recreation of a community nor improving the personal qualities of its residents? These questions are not asked here by enemies of the church, or by impractical reformers within its circle, or by armchair theorizers about its nature and function, but by a set of impersonal facts showing what the church is doing and failing to do in American cities.

Robert Cooley Angell (1951), of the University of Michigan, conducted a study with an objective similar to Thorndike's: to determine the factors responsible for the social health of a community, or, as Angell preferred to call it, the "moral integration" of a community. The "moral integration" index was constructed from two separate indices. One was the welfare effort of various cities, based upon statistics compiled in 1938 by the Children's Bureau, then under the U.S. Department of Labor. Angell's assumption was that cities where people were actively concerned with their neighbor's welfare could be considered to have a higher moral integration. The second index was based upon statistics for major crimes—murder, non-negligent manslaughter, robbery, and burglary—the thought being that a community that is morally knit together is not going to show high rates of violation of people and property. Reversing the scores for crime and adjusting them, he added these to the welfare effort index to arrive at his scale of moral integration, for 28 American cities. Using the 1936 Census of Religious Bodies, Angell tested the hypothesis that the larger the proportion of church members in a community, the better the moral integration. As in Thorndike's study, however, the hypothesis found no substantiation from the facts; communities with low church membership showed as much moral integration as did communities with high church membership. The author's conclusion: church membership, as such, is not a factor in determining the moral integration (or social health) of a city.

One other study might be cited, this confined to one specific aspect of social pathology, juvenile delinquency, and based upon a statewide sample of communities in Michigan. Weir (1941) tested the hypothesis that the greater the proportion of church members in a community the lower would be the rate of juvenile delinquency. As with the Thorndike and Angell studies, no significant correlation was found. In attempting to account for his results, Weir comments as follows:

Data on church membership are poor. . . . This may possibly be part of the reason why the proportion of the population claimed as church members is quite independent of the rate of juvenile delinquency ($r = -.16$). Yet this lack of significant association persists when other elements are eliminated from the picture.

CHURCH ATTENDANCE RELATED TO RELIGIOUS GROUPS AND SEX

We now examine one of the more traditional measures of religion, frequency of church attendance, for its possible relations to social and mental health. Some of our discussion and interpretations in this section are based on data provided especially for our use by Dr.

Gerald Gurin (1960), co-author of the Joint Commission's Monograph *Americans View Their Mental Health*. The study, conducted at the Survey Research Center of the University of Michigan, and involving interviews with a national sample of 2460 persons, was designed to gather basic information about the satisfactions, areas of distress, the kinds of problems, and ways of solving these problems, of the populace at large.

Table 1 shows the frequency of church attendance by religious groups and by sex, arranged in order of frequency of those attending once a week or more.

The membership figures for the six Protestant groups included here range from nearly 1.5 million (Congregational) to 19.5 million (27 Baptist bodies with 88,719 churches). Other religious bodies of over one million members each, besides Roman Catholic (34.5 mil-

Table 1—Frequency of Church Attendance by Religious Groups and by Sex

		Once a Week or More	Irregularly	Never	N.A.[a]	N
			PER CENT			
Catholic	Women	78	20	2		(304)
Catholic	Men	72	23	5		(238)
Fund.[b]	Women	64	32	2	2	(132)
Presbyterian	Women	51	41	8		(92)
All Protestant	Women	48	46	6		(1005)
Baptist	Women	47	47	6		(314)
Episcopalian	Women	47	47	6		(49)
Lutheran	Women	46	50	3	1	(110)
Other Prot.[c]	Women	46	48	6		(33)
Methodist	Women	44	50	6		(218)
Fund.[b]	Men	40	49	11		(91)
Congregational	Women	39	50	11		(28)
Congregational	Men	38	62	0		(21)
Lutheran	Men	32	62	6		(90)
Methodist	Men	28	63	8	1	(180)
All Protestant	Men	27	60	11		(740)
Other Prot.[c]	Men	25	70	5		(20)
Presbyterian	Men	23	58	19		(70)
Baptist	Men	22	60	8		(211)
Jewish	Men	14	59	27		(37)
Episcopalian	Men	10	55	35		(20)
Jewish	Women	5	76	17	2	(54)

[a] N.A.: "Not ascertained."

[b] "Fund." Includes members of Protestant Fundamentalist sect groups.

[c] "Other Prot." Includes members of Protestant denominations other than the six for which tabulations were made, but not members of Fundamentalist groups and small sects.

lion) and Jewish (5.5 million), are: Disciples of Christ, Churches of Christ, Christ Unity Science, Church of Jesus Christ of Latter Day Saints (Mormons), and Greek Orthodox. The national sample included insufficient numbers of these five and other groups for purposes of separate tabulation.

Frequency of church and synagogue attendance shows marked differences by religious group, particularly when adherents of the major faith groups—Protestant, Catholic, and Jewish—are compared. Catholic men and women both attend more frequently than others, followed by Protestants, with Jews (for whom many religious observances are centered in the home) showing the lowest level of regular attendance at worship. Women are much more frequent attenders than men, but the differences in attendance as related to sex are not as strong as the differences by major faith, since Catholic men and women are high in attendance, and Jewish men and women are both low in attendance.

CHURCH ATTENDANCE AND SELECTED INDICES OF MENTAL HEALTH

In this section we will examine some relations between frequency of church attendance and four selected indices, one direct and three indirect, of mental health: (1) the incidence rate for psychosis, (2) the relative frequency of affirmative and negative answers to the question as to whether one had ever felt he was about to have a nervous breakdown, (3) marital happiness, and (4) "over-all" happiness.

In considering the relation of church attendance to prevalence of psychosis as measured by the patient population, we take account of the fact that psychosis has been shown to be related to socioeconomic status. Persons with low incomes, little education, and who are in low prestige occupations offering low rewards tend to contribute more highly to the mental hospital patient population than do persons with the opposite socioeconomic characteristics (Hollingshead and Redlich, 1958).

There may be some oversimplification in relating mental illness to social class; the question arises here of the relative degree of "visibility" of mental illness in differing socioeconomic classes as an alternative to, or in addition to, true incidence. With this reservation in mind, if mental illness is related to education, income, and occupation, we should want to see what relation church attendance bears to these socioeconomic factors.

Church attendance shows an erratic picture for occupation and income. Education is the only class index portraying a consistent trend, with the more highly educated showing higher church attendance. If attendance were a significant factor in the prevention of psychosis, there should not be such differences in illness rates as those shown by the data of Frumkin (1955). For example, for every 100 persons in the managerial group who attend church a few times a year to never, Frumkin found 133 in that group who go to church once a week or more. For unskilled workers, there are 114 regular attenders for every 100 who go infrequently or not at all. Certainly these are not differences of any magnitude between the two groups. Yet, Frumkin's data show that unskilled male workers have a psychosis rate ten times as great as that for the managerial group; the rate for females is almost 25 times higher in the worker group than in the managerial.

In their study of mental illness in New Haven, Hollingshead and Redlich (1958) found that the prevalence rate of psychosis is eight times greater for the lowest class than it is for the two upper classes. Those earning under $3000 per year and those earning above $10,000 show roughly the same church attendance rates, but quite different psychosis rates. Going to church or not going, it would appear, is not so significant for mental health or for the prevention of mental illness, as the kind of home one returns to.

We may relate the specific index of religion under consideration here, frequency of church attendance, to an additional mental health variable by asking whether there is any relationship between frequency of church attendance and answers to the question: "Did you ever feel you were about to have a nervous breakdown?" (This question was among those asked of 2460 persons in the nationwide study by Gurin, Veroff and Feld referred to earlier.)

Little apparent relationship was found between frequency of

church attendance and having felt that one was about to have a nervous breakdown. Even when frequent and infrequent attenders are distributed by levels of education, we still find negligible differences.

When we arranged the sample by major income groups, we found that regular church attendance plus higher income appears to be a combination that shows a lower rate of affirmative answers to the question.

Two further mental health components, marital happiness and "general" happiness, also are subjective and, in a sense, oblique indices of mental health. Church attendance seems to be positively related to both marital happiness and to "general" happiness, but shows little or no relationship to whether an individual has or has not felt that he was about to have a nervous breakdown. But, church attendance is not so strongly associated with marital and over-all happiness as are the factors of education and income. In short, it seems to be more important for happiness to belong to the group with more income and more education than to the group with more frequent church attendance.

DIFFERING CHARACTERISTICS OF RELIGIOUS GROUPS

Two questions are often asked: whether one religious group shows higher mental illness rates than another; and whether any differences exist as to symptom choice—i.e., does one religious group show, for example, high suicide rates, while another shows high alcoholism rates? Rates of illness and type of illness have a great deal to do with factors other than religious affiliation. Education, income, occupation, ethnicity, place of residence, and age distribution are some of the factors that would have to be controlled and their influences understood for each religious group before a meaningful answer could be obtained.

Some Selected Socioeconomic Factors

Religious groups show great differences by education, occupation, and income, in other words, by social class. For example, for every 100 adult Baptists who hold college degrees, there are 1,360 adult

Baptists who have only a grade school education. At the other extreme, for every 100 Episcopalians who hold a college degree, there are 40 Episcopalians having only a grade school education. For every 100 "Fundamentalists" (in the previously mentioned national sample of 2460 persons) who have a yearly income of $15,000 or over, there are 7300 "Fundamentalists" who have incomes below $3000. For every 100 Episcopalians with a yearly income of $15,000 or over, there are 50 Episcopalians with incomes below $3000.

Baptists and "Fundamentalist" groups are predominantly low in income, in education, and in the number of persons in the professions. Episcopalians and Jews are proportionately higher in income, education, and occupation than are other groups. These findings confirm what is already well known: that religious groups differ greatly as to education, income, and occupation. And what is said about the mental health or illness of these groups must take these differences into account. In many instances it is impossible to separate the religious component from other components. For example, it is pertinent to ask whether these differences are religious or regional. Table 2 shows how each major Protestant denomination is distributed by geographic region. Sixty-seven per cent of the Baptists and 45 per cent of the "Fundamentalists" are in the South, while 61 per cent of the Congregationalists are in the Northeast. Table 3 shows the composition of each geographic region by religious group (Protestant only). The composition of each geographical region by

Table 2—Distribution of Protestant Denominations by Geographic Regions of the U.S.

Denomination	GEOGRAPHIC REGIONS				
	Northeast	Midwest	West	South	Total N
		PER CENT			
Baptist	9	13	11	67	(525)
Methodist	20	34	13	33	(398)
Lutheran	15	61	11	13	(200)
Presbyterian	23	33	18	26	(162)
Congregationalist	61	23	8	8	(49)
Episcopalian	33	23	16	28	(69)
Fundamentalist	6	39	10	45	(223)
Other Protestant	17	42	28	13	(53)
Other—N.A. if Fundamentalist	13	49	25	13	(8)

NOTE: All columns across total 100 per cent.

Table 3—Composition of Major Geographic Regions of the U.S. by Protestant Denominations

	GEOGRAPHIC REGIONS			
Denomination	Northeast	Midwest	West	South
		PER CENT		
Baptist	17	13	26	52
Methodist	29	26	25	19
Lutheran	12	24	10	4
Presbyterian	14	10	13	6
Congregationalist	11	2	2	*
Episcopalian	9	3	5	3
Fundamentalist	5	17	11	15
Other Protestant	3	4	7	1
Other—N.A. if Fundamentalist		1	1	
Totals	100	100	100	100
N =	(271)	(519)	(215)	(682)

Table 4—Composition of U.S. Geographic Regions by Major Faith Groups

	GEOGRAPHICAL REGIONS			
Religion	Northeast	Midwest	West	South
		PER CENT		
Protestant	46	79	71	92
Catholic	44	20	26	6
Jewish	10	1	3	2
Totals	100	100	100	100
N =	(612)	(687)	(330)	(749)

major faith is shown in Table 4. The South is 92 per cent Protestant, with the Baptists and "Fundamentalists" composing 67 per cent of the Protestant groups. With per capita personal incomes being lowest in the South (U.S. Department of Commerce, 1957), there is evidently a *regional* factor entering into the differences presented above.

Selected Mental Health Indices

Earlier we discussed the relation of church attendance to answers to the question, "Did you ever feel you were about to have a nervous breakdown?" Here we discuss the relation of church *affiliation* to affirmative and negative answers to this query. Table 5 shows answers to this question distributed by religious groups.

Catholics are somewhat lower than Protestants and Jews in affirmative responses, although the difference (seven per cent) is not

Table 5—Distribution by Religious Groups of Answers to the Question, "Have You Ever Felt You Were Going to Have a Nervous Breakdown?"

	Yes	No
Fundamentalist [a]	26	74
Other Protestant [a]	25	75
Baptist	22	78
Jewish	21	79
Protestant (total)	20	80
Presbyterian	20	80
Methodist	17	83
Lutheran	16	84
Roman Catholic	16	84
Congregational	16	84
Episcopalian	13	87

[a] See Table 1 for explanation of these designations.
Note that the eleven groups in this and following tables are those for whom attendance figures are reported in Table 1.

large. The only figures that do appear rather significant occur at the extremes; twice as many Fundamentalists as Episcopalians reported affirmatively.

Table 6 gives the extent of over-all happiness as reported by each group.

When we examine the extent of over-all happiness reported by religious groups, we find that both Baptists and Jews show 15 per cent in the "not too happy" response, a figure more than seven times as great as Congregationalists and almost four times as great as Episcopalians. Why six times as many Catholics as Congre-

Table 6—Extent of Happiness, by Religious Group

	Not too happy	Pretty happy	Very happy	Not Ascertained
		PER CENT		
Baptist	15	53	31	01
Jewish	15	51	32	02
Presbyterian	14	50	36	
Catholic	12	53	35	
Protestant (total)	11	54	35	
Fundamentalist	09	51	40	
Methodist	08	53	39	
Other Protestant	07	55	38	
Lutheran	06	64	30	
Episcopalian	04	47	49	
Congregational	02	49	49	

gationalists say they are "not too happy" is somewhat of an anomaly; it cannot be ascribed simply to class (which does correlate over-all with happiness, people with higher education and income reporting more happiness) since Jews and Baptists show class differences but not differences in happiness.

Table 7 presents an extent of worry index by religious groups. For every 100 Jews who report they never worry, 614 Jews say they worry a lot or always. At the other extreme, for every 100 Congregationalists who report they never worry, only 77 say they worry a lot or always. Unlike happiness, worry does not show a relationship to class (Gurin, 1960). Worry does not portray as much variation by religious group as does happiness or the demographic factors such as education, occupation, and income.

Religious groups vary greatly in terms of occupation, income, and education. They differ as well in degree of happiness, amount of worry, and the number who have felt they were about to have a nervous breakdown. These findings may be related to a definition of mental health, given by Jahoda (1958), as "the realization of a person's potential through action." In terms of this definition and these findings, the relevance for mental health of membership in one religious group or denomination rather than another would seem to lie less with such matters as creed and doctrine as with such factors as education, by virtue of which members of one group are in a better position to realize their potential than are members of another.

Table 7—Number of Persons Who Answered They Worry "Always" and "A Lot" for Every 100 Persons Who Answered "Never," by Religious Groups

Jewish	614
Baptist	457
Catholic	365
Other Protestant	267
Protestant (total)	265
Methodist	246
Fundamentalist	236
Presbyterian	235
Episcopalian	200
Lutheran	167
Congregational	77

The differences among Protestant groups are impressive, with Baptists and the respondents who have been grouped under "Other —Fundamentalist" showing consistent divergence from Episcopalians and to a lesser degree from Congregationalists. An implication of this finding is the caution that Protestants should not be grouped together for comparison with Catholic and Jews, since the divergence among Protestant denominations is greater than that between Protestants and other major faiths. A comparison of Jews, Catholics, and Protestants, wherein one group is found to be healthier than another, would risk masking the actual differences that exist within groups. The same reservation may well apply to differences within denominations.

Ways of Dealing with Stress

Coping (handling problems and crises by thought, action, and talking the problem over with the person involved), outside help (talking the problem over with someone other than the persons involved), and prayer are three major ways of dealing with stress. For every 100 Baptists who mention independent coping or seeking outside help as a first response, 78 mentioned turning to prayer. For every 100 Jews who mentioned independent coping or seeking outside help as a first response, one mentioned prayer. The extremes here resemble the class pattern, with Baptists and Fundamentalists at one end and Jews and Episcopalians at the other. Table 8 com-

Table 8—Number of Persons Who Use Prayer to Handle Periods of Worry, for Every 100 Who "Cope" or Use Outside Help, by Religious Group

Baptist	78
Fundamentalist	59
Other Protestant	55
Protestant (total)	44
Methodist	34
Lutheran	29
Congregationalist	23
Presbyterian	22
Catholic	22
Episcopalian	16
Jewish	1

pares the frequencies of prayer with independent coping and seeking outside help in periods of worry.

A class factor would seem to be operative here, since the use of prayer for handling periods of worry is greatest for the less educated, lower income groups (Gurin, *et al.*, 1960). The use of prayer is also higher for women than men, for older rather than young people, and increases with increase in church attendance, as might be surmised. Comparison of Tables 7 and 8 discloses that while Jews and Baptists report they worry about an equal amount, they differ radically in the ways they handle this worry, at least in regard to prayer versus problem-solving responses.

Table 9 gives the percentage of respondents, divided by religious group, who have had professional help for a mental health problem. Episcopalians and Baptists, who have thus far shown diverse tendencies, are here both low on having actually gone for professional help. Jews and "Other—Not Fundamentalist" have both gone for outside help with about equal frequency.

More significant differences occur, however, when we inquire who is seen as a potential source of help. Particularly relevant is the index presented in Table 10, which shows the number of persons who perceive the clergyman as a potential source of help for every 100 who see a psychiatrist as a source. For every 100 Catholics who mentioned a psychiatrist *only* (some persons mentioned more than one resource), there are 2020 Catholics who mentioned a clergyman. At the other extreme, for every 100 Jews who mentioned a psy-

Table 9—Percentage of Persons, by Religious Group, Who Have Had Professional Help for a Mental Health Problem

	PER CENT
Episcopalian	10
Baptist	11
Presbyterian	12
Fundamentalist	13
Protestant (total)	13
Methodist	13
Lutheran	14
Catholic	16
Congregationalist	16
Jewish	20
Other Protestant	21

Table 10—The Number of Persons, by Religious Group, Who Mentioned Clergy Only As a Potential Source of Help for Every 100 Who Mentioned Psychiatrist Only

Catholic	2,020
Lutheran	1,030
Baptist	1,000
Congregationalist	1,000
Fundamentalist	790
Protestant (total)	620
Methodist	540
Presbyterian	310
Other Protestant	260
Episcopalian	240
Jewish	40

chiatrist as a potential source of help, only 40 mentioned a clergyman. This corroborates what has been found by other researchers, that Jews are most inclined to seek help from psychiatrists, Protestants next, and Catholics least. The reciprocal would also seem to hold; namely, that Jews are least inclined to seek help from the clergy, Protestants next and Roman Catholics most likely.

Of the total respondents, 14 per cent have had help for emotional problems at some time in the past. Of these, 42 per cent have gone to members of the clergy for this help. In previous chapters, particularly those on pastoral counseling, we have dealt with some of the implications of these findings for the clergy as resources for mental health. We also take them into consideration in making the proposals in the next chapter.

We have now examined some relations between certain indices of religion and selected aspects of mental health. Two of the indices— membership and church attendance—have become traditional as methods of reporting and comparing degrees of religiousness. Two others are less traditionally used; these are the frequency of prayer in time of need, and the frequency of turning to a representative of religion, the clergyman.

When we examined the broad question of the relation of church membership to the social health of communities, we found little relevance from one to the other. Then, considering a somewhat more individual aspect of religion, attendance, we examined its relation to selected mental health factors such as prevalence of psychosis, marital happiness, "general" happiness, and the frequency with which people report that they have felt they were going to have a nervous breakdown. We related these in turn to educational and economic levels, finding that attendance showed some positive relation to happiness and the other indices of mental health, but that the socioeconomic factors, education and income, showed a stronger relation.

When we considered individual ways of dealing with stress, with particular reference to "coping," referring to outside help, and the more personal aspects of religion such as prayer, we discerned more significant relationships. Fuller consideration of these factors and of the individual's personal religious orientation and its relation to his mental health lay outside the scope of this study, but has entered into some of our suggestions for the church's efforts and emphasis in the area of mental health.

XIII

Directions and Strategy

In pointing to further ways in which the church's relevance for mental health can be strengthened, we take account of the most salient points of intersection between religion and mental health: the preparation of the clergyman in theological education; the person and work of the clergyman; the relations between the clergy and other mental health resources; the theoretical ground between religion (theology) and psychiatry; and the individual's religious beliefs, behavior, sentiments, and experience as they relate to mental health and illness.

THEOLOGICAL EDUCATION

In Chapter VII we described some of the trends in theological education, particularly in that aspect of it called clinical pastoral education, and some of the new departures and exploratory programs. Many clergymen, and psychiatrists as well, are concerned with ways in which theological education can be made to contribute more richly to making the pastor a resource for mental health. More courses in psychology, more clinical pastoral training—such recommendations run head on into the sheer weight of an already overcrowded curriculum, as well as the resistance of some faculties who would rather increase the offerings in "content" courses—theology, church history, philosophy of religion, Old and New Testament, and the like—than see the so-called "practical" courses proliferate. Alternative considerations have engaged the attention of educators in specific phases of theological education.

1. *Pre-theological Education*

Analogies can be found in prelegal and premedical training. The most useful preliminary studies prior to entering law school are considered to be not law courses, but English, history, and the like. Not only basic sciences, but also the humanities are seen as necessary prerequisites for medical school. While some familiarity with world religions, with religious thought, and with Scripture is desirable before entering theological school, a good background in the social sciences would seem to be equally if not more valuable, particularly in the psychology of personality, and in social processes and institutions. The future clergyman would then have a basic framework within which to do some further work in theological school either on a theoretical level, such as relating scientific and theological views of man, or on an empirical level, such as clinical pastoral training.

2. *Selection and Testing of Candidates for the Clergy*

Just what is "the call" to the ministry? Is it the voice of God? Or is it the product of subtle psychological forces? Or is it the voice of God working through subtle psychological forces? What conscious and unconscious factors motivate the decision? Is there any way of determining whether a student will make a good clergyman as early as his enrollment in the seminary? Considerable attention is currently being paid to these and many other questions concerning the motivation and selection of candidates for the ministry, the priesthood, and the rabbinate.

There is always present the danger that testing procedures applied to theological students, as to any other students, may be interpreted out of context, or may be overly imbued with charismatic authority. Yet, seen in perspective, they can participate in the total assessment of an individual, contribute to a further understanding of him, and add one more point of relative certainty in predicting his effectiveness in the ministry. Further, they can contribute to the growing body of information, factual and clinical data, and insight, of which more and more is still needed, as to what qualities in the individual tend to make a good clergyman.

Perhaps the effectiveness of the future clergyman should be assessed or predicted on the same basis as that of other graduate students aiming at other professions. F. Barron (1954), in *Personal Soundness in University Graduate Students,* describes the research in "excellence of human functioning" being conducted at the California Institute for Personality Assessment and Research. Personal soundness, which Barron describes as a way of reacting to problems and stresses rather than an absence of them, is related to "effectiveness and organization in working toward goals, correct perception of reality, character and integrity in the ethical sense, and interpersonal and intrapersonal adjustment." While some might well argue that certain other essentials are lacking from this roster— creativity, flexibility, spontaneity, or some more exclusively "clerical" or religious endowments such as sense of mystic identification or depth of "commitment"—no excellence in these last could be allowed to compensate for any deficiency in the four central traits.

Although there is some controversy, as well as ambivalence, regarding the value of tests, most theological seminaries have adopted one or more testing procedures, ranging from vocational interest questionnaires to depth interviews. Movements in this direction are exemplified in the work of William Bier, S.J., Ph.D., professor of psychology at Fordham University, who has adapted some of the standard projective techniques for use with seminarians. André Godin, S.J., of the Centre internationale pour la formation religieuse in Brussels, Belgium, has adapted the Thematic Apperception Test for use with religious orders. Gotthard Booth, M.D., has been instrumental in applying psychiatric interviews and other techniques to candidates in Episcopal theological schools. The Rev. Frederick Kling of the Educational Testing Service, Princeton, New Jersey, is conducting a long range study of the ministry as a profession for the National Council of Churches. In this study Mr. Kling is giving special attention to the motivation for entering the ministry both on the part of clergymen now in the ministry and on the part of theological students. William Alberts, Ph.D., while a graduate student at Boston University School of Theology, investigated attitudes of pastors toward the deviant, particularly the delinquent, and devised a testing instrument that discloses authoritarian characteristics in the personality of the pastor, a dimension which may prove to be of equal or more importance than some other aspects of the mental health of the clergy.

The foregoing are but a few examples of increasing attempts to gain a deeper understanding of the clergyman's motivation for choice of his profession, to acquire more insight into his personality, and to provide the most effective guidance for the student during his seminary career.

Motivation and selection are closely related to the total problem of the mental health of the clergy. The pastor who "breaks down" because of overwork may be overworking for some of the same reasons that underlie his breaking down. Rather than cause and effect, both may be related to common causes—which could be discerned and perhaps remedied if adequate testing procedures were used.

3. *Alternative and Additional Forms of Clinical Pastoral Training*

The most frequent and usual setting for clinical pastoral training is in the mental hospital. But both the Council for Clinical Training and the Institute of Pastoral Care sponsor training in general hospitals, and, less frequently, in correctional institutions. The Institute's training programs are nearly evenly divided between general and mental hospitals. Of the Council's 49 programs, most are conducted in mental hospitals; eleven are conducted in association with general hospitals, and seven in correctional institutions. Expansions of training programs to other social agencies and institutions would bring wider opportunities for theological students to have direct acquaintance with individual and social pathology and ways of dealing with it.

Suggestions have been put forward for changes in clinical pastoral training procedures in mental hospitals. Dr. Leon Saul, professor of Psychiatry in the University of Pennsylvania Medical School, advocates supervision by psychiatrists, rather than solely by chaplains or by chaplains and graduate student-chaplain supervisors. Dr. Saul also recommends at least twenty hours of personal analysis for each theological student in training. While in many cases carrying out such recommendations would prove to be not feasible, the suggestions remain as a goal.

We would advocate training in the parish itself as an alternative, or in addition. Supervised field work is the custom in most theological seminaries; and the so-called "intern year" has been tried in a few, with varying degrees of success. The further step—intensive clinical training in the parish setting— would enable the student to encounter a cross section of the problems he will face in his own pastoral work later. Were such training to be designed in such a way that it could be called "clinical," it would involve first-hand contact and experience in dealing with people in trouble and in serenity, in sickness and in health, and, in addition, the continual opportunity to examine and discuss and digest these experiences with the help of a highly trained supervisor—pastor, psychologist, or faculty member. Only with the help of such an ongoing process between student and supervisor, or, as second choice, in a small group, can a genuine learning experience occur.

THE ROLE AND IDENTITY OF THE CLERGYMAN

One of the questions we asked the psychiatrists whom we interviewed (see Chapter XI) dealt with their views of the best ways the clergy could foster the mental health of their parishioners. To summarize, psychiatrists suggest that the clergy: emphasize the pastoral function of the ministry; serve as good models; listen skillfully; recognize danger signals; concentrate on the spiritual welfare of the parishioners; and understand their own limitations as clergymen as well as their most proper and effective functions.

It is significant that the psychiatrists see the clergy as of most potential help in mental health matters in the pastoral role, primarily in the one-to-one pastoral counseling relationship, which resembles in some respects the psychiatrist-patient relationship. While the content of the communication may be different, the overt structure of the role they visualize for the pastor as he functions at his maximum usefulness is similar to their own. A further implication is that for the psychiatrists there seems to be no conflict, no jealousy, no rejection of the pastor visualized in a role that, at least outwardly, resembles that of the psychiatrist in his relation with the patient.

This does not give the pastor carte blanche to attempt to take on the role, identity, and function of the psychiatrist. The renewal of pastoral counseling in the mid-twentieth century is due to many factors. On the part of laymen the demand for pastoral counseling may express a deep need for personalizing the relationship with an institution which has become impersonal. The response on the part of the clergy may reflect a need to redefine, restructure, and recenter a role which has threatened to become tangential. The warm acceptance and appreciation the psychiatrists express for the contribution of the clergy is tempered by their qualifications: concentrate on the spiritual welfare of the parishioner; understand your limitations and functions.

What are the most significant and effective functions of the clergy? In the remainder of this section we will examine some aspects of this question in order to delineate further feasible programs and areas of emphasis for the churches' attention.

As a resource for mental health, the strength of the clergy—from the point of view of numbers—lies in the parishes, in the communities. Unlike psychiatrists, the parish clergy are well represented geographically, and are available to persons irrespective of class or socioeconomic and educational levels. There are indeed many counties and sections of the country where the clergy are the only resources to whom individuals can appeal for help with problems. Although there are some barriers to ready accessibility to the clergy, such as the image of the church as the "community of the elect," or the anticipation that a clergyman may be moralistic, judgmental, or punitive, there seems to be less psychological distance between layman and clergyman than between layman and psychiatrist or other professional mental health resources.

The effectiveness of the clergyman often depends on the degree of congruence of his self-image with the perception of him held by his parishioners. As we have noted earlier, the clergy are in considerable conflict regarding their appropriate role in dealing with the mentally ill. In the mental hospital chaplaincy, for example, they find themselves in a situation in which they are limited in number and capacity, as well as in ratio to other personnel. Furthermore, the chaplaincy is in a situation in which the church has no real control, with state control of the mental hospital raising a church-state problem. The church-supported hospitals devoted exclusively to the care of the mentally ill are a small minority (21 in all, of which 8 are Protestant and 13 Roman Catholic). Though the value of the chaplain's work is undisputed, the patients with whom we talked do not see the clergy as a source of help toward recovery. (We have suggested earlier that the churches should explore the possibility of supplying as many chaplains as the states themselves support.) Further, the money spent by the churches in the area of health is allocated primarily to children, to the aged, and to the alleviation of physical suffering—poverty, hunger, and, to some extent, some organic diseases. Thus while the work of the 400 mental hospital chaplains is significant and needs to be expanded and strengthened in any way possible, direct work with the mentally ill, though it represents the most sharply focused aspect of "the churches and mental health," may be somewhat peripheral to the *total* task of the ministry.

There are 21 church-related mental hospitals, slightly over 4 per cent of a nation-wide total of 496 mental hospitals; and these 21 receive 3.7 per cent of all mental hospital admissions. There are 1115 church-related or church-operated general hospitals, according to the *Yearbook* of the American Hospital Association (1958). These represent 20 per cent of the total of 5546 general hospitals in the nation, and receive 30 per cent of all general hospital admissions.

A substantial number of church-related *general* hospitals admit patients for the diagnosis and treatment of mental and emotional disorders. Of the 5546 general hospitals, 505, or almost 11 per cent, admit psychiatric patients. Of these 176, or 35 per cent, are church-related (105, or 21 per cent, of the total are Roman Catholic; 71, or 14 per cent, are Protestant.) Since church-related general hospitals constitute only 20 per cent of all general hospitals but represent 35 per cent of all general hospitals admitting psychiatric patients, it is apparent that church-related general hospitals are favorably represented as psychiatric resources.

Comparison of the 3.7 per cent of church-supported admissions to mental hospitals with the 18.6 per cent church-supported admissions to psychiatric services in general hospitals indicates that the psychiatric services in general hospitals are much better supported by the churches and, accordingly, may lie closer to the interests of religious groups than do the mental hospitals. In assessing their directions and strategy for mental health, the churches would do well to examine closely the possibility of a more intensive ministry to the general hospital, with special attention to those that have psychiatric units, since this is where a fair portion of their financial support and, to some extent, personnel, in the form of chaplains, is already allocated.

While continuing to support chaplaincy programs and work with the mentally ill, the clergy might well explore ways to capitalize on their strength and work primarily in the areas of the "normal," rather than the pathological. A starting point might be the children, and other close relatives, of the mentally ill, and also members of homes broken or disturbed in other ways—by crime, alcoholism, divorce or desertion, as well as by mental illness. Such a program would harmonize with the function, resources, and accessibility of the clergy. In this way, concentrating upon the "well," the "normal," the clergy would serve as a first line of defense in the control of mental illness, preventing the "flow" of further damage to persons who are touched by mental illness in this way. As in the epidemiology of other communicable illnesses, one must take account of the agent, the host, and the environment. In this case, the clergy would be giving special attention to the potential "host," an object of concern that is often overlooked. Seeing the clergy—and encouraging them to see themselves—in such supportive and informational roles may be more realistic than hoping to see them as one answer to the manpower shortage in the direct care and treatment of the mentally ill.

COMMUNICATION

1. *Interprofessional*

Much of the communication between clergy and individuals and institutions representing sources of help for the troubled seems to be oblique rather than direct, sporadic rather than continual and flowing, on a theoretical rather than a clinical basis, and formalized —limited to, or at least concentrated in, occasional symposia and "workshops"—rather than personal and spontaneous. Yet the process of referral, to point to only one area of the relationship between clergy and mental health resources, is greatly facilitated if it takes place within a context of already established relationships. Communication between clergy and psychiatrists is promoted by such organizations as the Academy of Religion and Mental Health, which now numbers many clergymen, psychiatrists, and social scientists among its members. Yet even under the auspices of some interdisciplinary movements, it is less likely to be the "working clergy" who communicate with social scientists than a limited number of theological faculty members.

The responsibility for communication does not rest solely with the clergy. Psychiatrists and other behavioral scientists, if they would accelerate the trend towards utilization of the community's total resources in fostering mental health, also have an obligation to seek better communication, both direct and indirect, with the clergy. A considerable contribution would be to make available to the parish clergy, with particular reference to the vast majority of them who have had no clinical pastoral training, good information dealing with the recognition of symptoms of mental disorders. Some mental health associations attempt to keep the clergy informed about community resources and channels of referral. This service could be implemented by local councils of churches, diocesan information offices, and the like, taking responsibility for the distribution of information made available by mental health agencies.

2. *Intra-professional*

Communication gaps exist not only between the clergy and other professions, but also within the clergy between members of the major faith groups and between denominations. The cleavages extend in many directions and dimensions—between fundamentalists and liberals, between theologians and pastoral psychologists, and between the theologically oriented and the psychologically oriented among the "working clergy." There would seem also to be poor communication in general from pastor to pastor in the community, as reflected in the responses to our questions to clergy throughout the country. The isolation, or poor communication, from clergy to clergy, and from clergy to other professions related to the mental health field, may be a symptom of a generally low state of health of the clergy themselves, if good communication is an indication of good health.

3. *Pastoral*

Good communication is not limited to its verbal aspects. There are many ways in which the pastor communicates with members of his congregation in addition to his weekly sermon. A subtle aspect of the communication between clergyman and layman concerns potentialities of the relationship developed in the counseling situation. There is always some ambivalence about approaching people in a technical, skillful way, and in an understanding, loving way. Some relationships remain, or can become, only functional, with the focus on "what he can do for me," and vice versa. While we tend to associate the doctor or the psychiatrist or the scientist with the technical approach and the clergyman with the loving, understanding approach, quite the opposite may be true in some cases. That is, the scientist may be best able to focus on the person and upon the care of the person independent of his utility; while the clergyman may unknowingly establish a functional relationship based on his expectation that, as the only form of recompense he anticipates, his counselee will attend church more regularly or support it more fully. The psychiatrist's recompense is clearcut and definite, and his perception of his patient is unambiguous. The clergyman, on the other hand, may perceive the counselee under many aspects. He may see him in one or more of his roles in the community or in his relationships in the church group. He may perceive him as troubled, as sinful, as unreligious. He may see him as one of his "flock," or even as one of his employers. He may see him as a "pew-filler," one to be counted, one whose anticipated increased religiousness will not be for his own sake, or for God's sake, but for the sake of the pastor. Any one or more of these may predominate, and may contribute to determining the counseling relationship as a functional or utilitarian one.

INTERVENTION: CRISIS AND PRE-CRISIS, LONG RANGE AND SHORT RANGE

Pastoral counseling and other similar functions of the clergyman may be considered largely as preventive steps, rather than remedial, or treatment procedures. Group or individual counseling can often serve as a stabilizing factor. The relationship with the pastor, and with others in the group or congregation, is often supportive and sustaining. The counseling, discussion, and the like can provide for the discharge of tensions and worries, and for talking out problems and conflicts that might otherwise lead to more serious mental and emotional states.

There is always present the risk that the relief obtained through pastoral counseling may cover over and otherwise disguise deeply-lying emotional conflicts and personality needs. This risk can be reduced by providing the clergy with information and understanding, preferably through training and some variety of clinical experience, so that they can more readily recognize symptoms of pathology and also so that they can have enough insight to see clearly the limits of their own competence. In the long run the risk seems worth taking, particularly when it is weighed against the woefully inadequate professional manpower and facilities available for treatment. Under these circumstances merely covering over deep-seated conflicts can be a major service.

Though we may acknowledge that the clergyman's maximum effectiveness is in the area of prevention rather than treatment, when we perceive him as a counselor, or as a referral agent, or even as a "clergy-consultant" acting in conjunction with mental health resources, we are still talking about his function on a secondary level of prevention. The "primary level" of prevention, while a profoundly complicated matter, would see the clergy facilitating the maximum contribution of religion to the growth of whole, mature persons—creative, adventuresome, able to give and receive love fully, with long-range orientations and aspirations.

Even when we acknowledge that dealing with disturbed or perplexed people is not the primary content of the clergyman's function and that mental health is not the goal but only a hoped-for and fortuitous by-product of religion, we still need to exercise care to avoid the dangers of causal inference. For there may be no relation between religion and mental health in the sense of causation.

In addition to glandular, neural, genetic, and other organic and chemogenic factors which may be related to mental disorder, many environmental factors affect both intra-personal and inter-personal states. We do not know to what extent a seemingly mature, non-utilitarian, intrinsic religious orientation (see Introduction) could overcome the effects of pathogenic relationships in the early experience of the individual that might tip the balance toward the possibility of mental disorder. (Of course, granted the prior traumatic experiences and relationships with parents, other adults or other authority and superego figures, the chances for a "mature," "internalized" religion in the individual's later life are somewhat remote.)

Will a good orientation with the universal, the unknown, the good, with God, be likely to undo the negative effects of a poor orientation with the local, the particular, the known, the bad, the stupid and insensitive? Although we still know little about constitutional predisposition to mental illness, it appears that much mental and emotional disturbance is caused, it doesn't just happen; and it is caused in the complex of relationships with other people. The highest potential that may be inherent in the relation between religion and mental health, and in the preventive role of the clergyman, may be to draw upon the insights of religion and of psychology so as to relate with other people, particularly with children, in a way that avoids, to as great a degree as possible, the kinds of relationships and behavior that, subtly at work over a long period of time, tend to be predisposing—if not precipitating—factors to mental disorder.

The clergy must not only capitalize on certain natural, built-in aspects of their role—such as accessibility—but they must achieve, and maintain, both perspective and humility. As they must co-operate, in what we have called "secondary prevention," with psychiatrists and other mental health resources, and often relinquish parishioners to them, so in "primary prevention" the clergy must realize that religion is only one aspect of the individual's total value system and orientation, and be able to discern that in the long-range growth process, other factors may be as important as religion, other institutions as important as church and synagogue, and other figures —parents, teachers—as important as the clergy. The over-responsibility observable on the part of many clergymen may be due less to an innate compulsiveness than to a lack of perspective on this point.

Having made it clear that we do not claim an exclusive function for religion or for the clergy, we can focus for the moment on intervention in crisis, or pre-crisis, situations, and on the need for the clergy to devise new ways—and recapture old ways—to "intervene."

Intervention, in the sense in which we are using the term, involves the pastor being available in his role as a pastor rather than trying to be something else. His personality, his insight, his sensitivity may prove to be even more important at such times than any psychological training and technical skills he might have acquired. To insure timely and effective intervention, clergymen often can benefit by supplementing their natural capacity and their availability through cooperation with social scientists in clarifying the concept of health, in constantly redefining what Margaret Mead calls the "moving target," mental health. They need to be alert to signs of mental and emotional disturbance, but also to the differences between effective and ineffective coping. Effective coping, and effective intervention, may involve dealing with short-range crises in such a way as not to become predisposed to deal uncreatively with future crises. This ability may indeed be a key characteristic of mental health.

Iago Galdston, M.D. (1957), describes "crisis" as

a subject which has engaged the best intellects in both ancient and modern times. Save for those religious teachers who saw in human experience the inscrutable will of the deities, the keenest students of humanity have looked upon individual crisis as the manifestation of "life at cross-purpose." Crises, excluding those resulting from that order of disaster so irreverently termed acts of God, were traced to their antecedents—to *ubris* (wanton violence arising from pride of strength). Crisis thus was "nemesis—ripened in the womb of time." Not withdrawal into total abnegation, but rather a more ample comprehension and fulfillment of the objective and moral relationship of man to man and of man to the transcending meanings of life was the way to salvation taught by the Greek moral philosophers, by the Hebrew prophets, and by Christ.

What further effective ways can be found in which the churches can help to provide this "more ample comprehension and fulfill-ment"?

A crisis can be long-range or short-range, an episode or a condi-tion, emergency or contingent, a turning point or a terminal point. Many of the major crises of life are surrounded, defined, acknowl-edged by appropriate religious ceremonies and rituals designed to express joy, as in baptism, circumcision, communion, Bar Mitzvah, marriage, or to express, control, and ritualize grief, as in bereave-ment. In the crises of continuity, as well as in the disruptive crises, the church has on the one hand emphasized and strengthened the continuity bridged by the "happy" crises, and on the other allayed and minimized the discontinuity of the disruptive crises by giving them further meaning and providing for the full expression of sor-row within the context of the church's tradition.

Many life crises and changes may also be "ritualized" in less overt ways. Mental illness may in a sense be viewed as one of these life crises ("passages") whose trauma, for both the patient and his family, may be reduced by appropriate "rites of passage." This does not imply some kind of formal ceremony, but rather the more subtle ritualization of the crisis through a pre-established relationship with the religious body and with the religious figure, a relationship which, though latent, can become manifest and intensified.

There are many less defined crises, often of a long-term nature, barely discernible as crises, which go unrecognized and in which the individuals concerned are often left to fend for themselves. The effects of marital stress, for example, are compounded where no mechanisms are present to minimize the effect on the children. The clergyman can sometimes intervene in such situations, providing a source of support, a means of opening up blocked communication, as a substitute for the intervention formerly available from the "extended family." Alcoholism, crime, and delinquency, though they may be focused in specific acts, are usually long-term, situational crises and expressions of personal, familial, or social disorganization. The clergyman can give timely support and help to the "deviant," whether in the community, in an institution, or returning to his family, as well as to his family members.

The problems of the aging are receiving more attention now than formerly, from both medicine and the clergy. The compensatory and adjustment mechanisms that come into play when faculties and capacities decline are sometimes more productive of crises and critical situations than the aging process itself. In earlier times in our society, and in some other societies today, the family, and often the community, turned to its aged members as a source of wisdom, strength, and counsel. Today, advanced age seems to be more associated with retirement, with hobbies, with social security—or, at the most, with baby sitting. There are many ways in which church and synagogue can make aging a more creative experience—as by giving responsibility to the aging in the religious group, and by extension, in home and community, thus providing more of a sense of meaning and significance to their lives.

Times of crisis that are infrequently foreseen when the individual concerned is left without adequate help, are the period following childbirth, the menopause, and the climacteric. Though biochemical processes are in part responsible for disruptions at these times, the bewilderment, even the depressive states, can be relieved by intelligent support. Further, a clergyman with an understanding of what is taking place can secure medical or psychiatric help for his parishioner.

In time of personal or family crisis, it is often four to six weeks before some sort of equilibrium is attained, according to Dr. Gerald Caplan of the Harvard School of Public Health. And the equilibrium achieved may be at a higher or lower level than that which prevailed before the crisis was precipitated. As an example, Dr. Caplan points to the individual who may seem to be coping satisfactorily with a crisis, yet whose perception and appreciation of the needs of others in the family and whose ability and willingness to satisfy them may be greatly impaired. Continuity of communication is thus interrupted. A clergyman who has a "built-in" accessibility to people in his community, particularly his own parishioners, and who is familiar with the range of ways in which people solve their problems, can slow down, and sometimes prevent, this subtle process of alienation.

This does not imply that we recommend that the clergyman supply a psychiatric type of intervention, but simply do what a wise, humane individual can do. Often people are helped by a simple action: sometimes just listening, or talking, or being present. Direct, simple, supportive action at the right time is often more useful than the most skillful psychotherapy at the wrong time. It is often less a question of "how" or "what," than simply a matter of "that"—that the intervention occurred, that the help was offered.

Another kind of "crisis"—long-range, and often unrecognizable as such—is one in which we see the "marginal" person who is living on the edge of life, who is in danger of dropping out of the human race for the time being at least—out of the family, out of society— who is close to getting lost, or to being unable to hold on to the normal self. His plight is aptly described by Harold G. Wolff, Professor of Psychiatry at Cornell University Medical College (1959, p. 39):

The goal-directed individual who fails to attain his goals calls upon a number of adaptive devices. These defenses are evident in both behavior and attitude. For example, he pretends the situation is other than it is. . . . He blames others or something outside himself. He explains away or rationalizes or puts his failure in the category of abstraction, where it is less offensive. He becomes overly busy in directions that are not appropriate but that nevertheless accord immediate satisfactions and therefore tranquilize or temporarily allow him to continue in his threatened state; or failing in any or all of these, he may invoke that most ominous one, the depersonalization pattern in which an individual figuratively pulls down the curtain and acts as if he cannot see the danger. Failing in all of these defenses, he may then pass through a state that I have called, for lack of a better word, one of nonadaptation or the "unadapted phase." This is an extremely dangerous state, in which the person's defenses are operating only intermittently and in which he is aware of an uneasy, insecure, or anxious feeling, in which his thinking is slowed and impaired, in which his capacity to make a decision as to direction and activity seems to be blocked.

While failure to attain goals and similar disillusionments are commonplace though subtle crises, the defenses and adaptive devices described by Dr. Wolff are met in many other seemingly subcritical situations. Extra-punitiveness, rationalization, abstraction, tranquilization by inappropriate overaction, and depersonalization patterns, are in themselves potentially dangerous, and more so when, these defenses having proven unsatisfactory, the individual abandons them and slips into the "nonadaptive" phase. Again intervention at some preclinical level may successfully and safely interrupt the process. The clergyman, within an established relationship of concern and knowledge, can function as the intervener in such a process, as well as in the ordinary predicaments of life and upsets of equilibrium, often without waiting to be called.

For the most effective crisis, pre-crisis, or post-crisis intervention on the part of the clergyman, there appear to be two prerequisites. The first concerns the clergyman's maximum personal effectiveness (and we refer here particularly to the majority of clergymen, who have no formal clinical training). If he can discern subtle pre-clinical symptoms of stress, of decreasing communication, of increased isolation, his help will be all the more timely. He should be aware of the dangers of such cues; but insight, knowledge, clinical experience, common sense—none of these will be of use unless he is accessible. Further, he needs to be flexible and see the potentialities for help in many kinds of relationships and not just in formal counseling. Perhaps the clergy can recapture a kind of "kitchen counseling" as an alternative to the "swivel-chair" counseling so much the vogue today.

The second prerequisite concerns the prior establishment of a social-pastoral relationship; that is, the value of a long-range relationship with a religious group and tradition. This does not mean that a clergyman will not intervene in a family or individual situation where the individual is not a member of his church. But a great potential seems to lie in an established relationship of the individual with the church or religious community, so that when crises occur, they will occur within an already established continuity of orientation and meaning.

We have referred to both meaning and continuity. They are closely related. Some hold that the contribution from religious counseling in contradistinction to secular is the orientation within a frame of meaning. A rabbi (see Chapter VII) urges the clergyman not to limit his goals in counseling to helping the counselee see his way to make decisions and resolve conflicts, but to help him find meaning and purpose in his life. The director of a counseling center (see Chapter VI) tells us that one of the most persistent and predominant problems among his male counselees is a sense of lack of meaning.

But, in this context, what is the significance of "meaning"? Is it a question only of some kind of cosmic orientation? Or is it a question of acquiring an orientation towards long-range objectives, an orientation within which upsets of equilibrium, failures to reach goals, and other disturbances can be placed in context? How is the religious counselor to escape remaining problem-centered in dealing with individuals and work effectively in the realm of meaning and purpose?

Certain aspects of existential analysis offer added perspective and dimensions to this issue. Henri F. Ellenberger, co-editor with Rollo May (1958) of *Existence,* says, "What we call the feeling of the 'meaning of life' cannot be understood independently of the subjective feeling of experienced time."

To illuminate his argument, Ellenberger summarizes Eugene Minkowski's analysis of the zones of experienced time, which are to be distinguished from chronological time, and which for the normal individual constitute a structural unit, though each is experienced in a different way. The seven zones are:

The remote past, or zone of the obsolete; the mediate past, or zone of the regretted; the immediate past, or zone of the remorse; the present; the immediate future, or zone of expectation and activity; the mediate future, or zone of wish and hope; the remote future, or zone of prayer and ethical action.

While "each of these zones must be experienced in a specific fashion in order to fit into our normal experience of time," various distortions can occur. In such long-range crisis situations as prolonged unemployment, for example, "individuals may become unable to experience the 'immediate future' " (expectation and activity), this resulting in a gap between the present and the other two future zones, "a stagnation in a hypertrophic and sterile present and an inability to organize their lives in a constructive way."

"Distortions of the feeling of time," Ellenberger continues (May, 1958, pp. 106–108):

necessarily result in distortions of the meaning of life. Normally we look upon the future not only for itself but also for compensating and correcting the past and the present. We reckon on the future for paying our debts, achieving success, enjoying life, becoming good Christians. Whenever the future becomes empty, as with manics and certain psychopaths, life is a perpetual gamble and the advantage of the present minute is taken into consideration; whenever the future is inaccessible or blocked, as with the depressed, hope necessarily disappears and life loses all meaning. . . . The outlook on the future and the past involves the length of time that comes under our full awareness. . . . We feel that time flows not only for us but also for the rest of the world. Our personal time must be *inserted into the social, historical, and cosmic time.*

While it seems reasonable to suppose that, as Gordon Allport (1958) expresses it, "a comprehensive, meaningful, and satisfying world view, such as a mature religion provides, would unify and direct a life and thus prevent its disintegration in the face of disruptive forces," we still lack any proof, empirical or otherwise, for this assumption. An ancient root of the word "religion" means to bind, to fasten, to tie. A sense of binding, of relatedness between the flow of time *for me* and for humanity, for the universe, may be a key aspect of religion in this ancient sense, and may provide a link between the comprehensive world view that a mature religion can provide, and the clear perception and relatedness of past, present, and future, without which the experience of time—and thus the meaning of life—becomes distorted.

It is not possible to give here an adequate account of existentialism and its relevance for mental health. It is an important movement— as one psychologist described it, "part fad, part a legitimate seeking for a more intrinsic ground of contact with the religious view of man's lot." The insights we have referred to in our necessarily fragmentary account, derived from phenomenology and existential analysis, would seem to have considerable relevance for religion as well as for mental health. They give important cues for the clergy, as they deal with the specific life and problems of the specific individual, and as they re-examine and re-shape the goals and strategy of their total ministry.

OBSERVATION, EXPLORATION, AND RESEARCH

While there are important problems to be explored in the critical area traversed by theology and psychiatry, we limit our suggestions here to the more personal and empirical areas of our topic. Much observation and exploration still needs to be done on a descriptive level before interpretative or analytic studies can be undertaken. Research does not have to be limited to a formal design, with tested and pre-tested research instruments, a sophisticated sampling procedure, experimental and control groups, and other highly scientific qualifications. The words, *observation, exploration, research,* were chosen deliberately in order to expand and loosen the concept of research often held by those who peer in through the windows of the social science "laboratory," as well as by some of those who peer out.

Nor need the researcher be limited to the statistician. Fruitful insights, it is true, have been derived with the help of such statistical procedures as correlation matrices, and even from simple counting. Still more have been found by "hovering," as it were, over a single case history.

In considering proposals for further exploration of the churches and mental health it is well to keep in mind the personnel and facilities available for such research. Otherwise, suggestions can become impractical and unrealistic. There are two major divisions of resources: lay (or secular), and clerical (or religious). The secular resources include psychologists (social and clinical), psychiatrists, anthropologists, and other social scientists. Much of the research being done by social scientists is centered in the graduate schools that produce them; and this is the source of most of the current research in religion.

There are two basic weaknesses inherent in this situation. First, most graduate students undertaking research use the most readily available research subjects; that is, members of the student body. This procedure automatically excludes diversity in age, education, socioeconomic levels, and the like. Second, little communication takes place between secular researchers in the social sciences and the clergy. Thus, little of the significant research taking place in universities and clinics and published in scholarly journals, which are read almost exclusively by members of the respective specialty, comes to the attention of the clergy.

On the clerical side there are four categories of personnel available.

1. *The parish clergy.* Most are untrained in research methods. But, as we emphasized earlier, "method" is not absolutely indispensable to good research. Most clergymen are too busy to undertake any specific research program. But all could find some benefit—both to themselves and to others of their profession with whom they could communicate, through published articles, conferences, and the like—from an exploratory and observational approach, a "research attitude," to their own work.

2. *The institutional clergy.* There are several groups included in this rubric: (a) the religious, i.e., members of religious orders; (b) military chaplains; (c) university and college chaplains; and

(d) chaplains in mental hospitals, general hospitals, correctional institutions, and the like.

To select only the last for discussion: In the mental hospital the only information "officially" acquired concerning a patient's religion is his church membership. Yet the chaplain may have a vantage point from which to do fruitful research in the area of religion and psychopathology.

Orville Walters, M.D., of the University of Illinois, holds that study of the religion of the schizophrenic can add little to the understanding of the religion of normal people. In a review of American and English research in religion and psychosis, Michael Argyle (1959, pp. 119–120), Lecturer in Social Psychology at the University of Oxford, finds no evidence that psychotics are either more or less religious than "normal" persons, although about one-seventh have a definite religious content to their disorder:

The bizarre religious ideas of psychotics are derived from traditional religion, distorted into idiosyncratic self-referential versions under the influence of intense motivation. The ideas aid in the interpretation of the experiences as religious, the experiences support the beliefs. General causal theories exaggerate the extent of the relation between religion and mental disorder, and give no evidence concerning the direction of causation.

To take account of such reservations as the foregoing before suggesting that the chaplain engage in research is only prudent. Few studies at any depth have been done in religion and psychosis. Among them can be counted the investigations by Anton Boisen, chaplain at Elgin State Hospital, and by Wayne Oates, professor of the Psychology of Religion at Southern Baptist Theological Seminary.

The chaplain who is alert to research possibilities can contribute in two areas in which further exploration is greatly needed: in regard to the patient—his religious orientation, beliefs, symbolism, experience, and their relation, if any, to his illness; and in regard to the chaplain—assessment and evaluation of his role, his relations to patients, staff and community, with the goal of maximizing his effectiveness.

3. *Research bureaus of religious organizations and agencies.* The

Bureau of Research and Survey of the National Council of Churches, for example, as well as those of several State and city councils of churches, include on their staffs highly competent social scientists. The work of most church council research departments, however, is often oriented toward community-wide surveys for such purposes as guidance in locating future churches and similar strategy and planning. A few exceptions, notable among them the National Council's research department, have sufficient staff and scope to explore other aspects of religion.

4. *Departments of psychology, "pastoral theology," etc.* Such departments in theological schools encourage empirical research by candidates for masters and doctoral degrees. Dissertations for the B.D. degree rarely require research in the sense in which we are using the term. The theological school could become both a resource for first-rate research in religion and personality, and a "bending of the twig," committing the future clergyman to an "observation-exploration-research" orientation throughout the course of his ministry.

In an address before the National Association for Mental Health, Jack R. Ewalt, M.D., Professor of Psychiatry in Harvard Medical School, and Director of the Joint Commission on Mental Illness and Health, called for "unorthodox research" in the field of mental health. The attempt to explore the area crossed by the concerns, values, viewpoints, and techniques of religion and of mental health is no doubt in itself unorthodox. Depending on one's point of view, this area seems to be either a no-man's land, to be crossed trembling, or an Everyman's land, hospitable to all travelers.

Certain queries can be made that will serve the double purpose of spying out the land and indicating lines of investigation: What perspectives can be brought to bear on mental health, on personality, from the point of view of religion and of theology? What perspectives can be brought to bear on religion from the point of view of mental health, mental hygiene, psychology, psychiatry, psychoanalysis, ego psychology, existential analysis? Do religion, the church, the clergy have anything to offer mental health?

Do we gain from a religious understanding of behavior? Does the mental health movement have anything to offer religion, the church, the clergy? Do we gain from a psychological understanding of religion? Can the two viewpoints, and the multiple philosophies subsumed under each, be brought to a focus in a theological-psychological understanding of man?

Some research problems that seem to be accessible from the viewpoints and techniques of both religion and mental health are currently being formulated by the non-sectarian, interdisciplinary Religious Education Association. Some of the nation's most distinguished social scientists are cooperating with leading theologians, pastoral psychologists, and religious educators in an exploration and formulation of long-range research plans. Following are a few of the sixteen broad areas into which the more than one hundred research problems already delineated naturally fall:

1. Concepts of man in the cultural milieu, and their bearing on religious and character formation.

2. The communication of these concepts, and of religious ideas, patterns of living, and ethical ideals.

3. Developmental stages in religious and character formation.

4. Problems of religious as versus secular culture.

5. The nature of religious experience.

6. The nature and role of the family, parents, marriage and sex mores as they relate to personality development.

While most of the problems are related tangentially to mental health, many are related directly. Among them are many on which religionists and social scientists can collaborate creatively.

When we inquire into the relevance of religion for mental health, we bear in mind the reservation made earlier that mental health is to be seen not solely as the goal of religion, but as a fortunate by-product. More important than inquiring how religion can contribute to the mental health of the individual may be the question of how religion can add a dimension for understanding and assessing mental health; what it can add to the criteria for health, for the healthy person.

Specific suggestions for research would embrace the following areas:

1. *The effect and effectiveness of clinical pastoral training.* Does clinical training (described in Chapter VII) make a more effective clergyman? Does it make him more effective in counseling troubled parishioners?, in understanding them?, in self-understanding?

The only published study that attempts to evaluate clinical training is that by Ernest Bruder and Marian Barb (1956) in which clergymen were asked, ten years afterward, what they thought about the effects of their clinical training experience. While this subjective study has value, no objective study has been done.

2. *Research specifically on pastoral counseling.* There are still a number of major areas of pastoral counseling where descriptive studies have yet to be done. There is little material available yet on the extent of counseling by either the Roman Catholic or Jewish clergy. (See Schnitzer, 1958.) The few descriptive studies on the Protestant clergy's counseling have to date included only urban and suburban ministers, and have not yet touched upon counseling by rural pastors. Useful additions to our knowledge might be turned up when these studies are made.

Another area of pastoral counseling that awaits descriptive measurement is that done by the nonparish clergy. This broad field includes the military, prison, and hospital chaplaincies; the counseling of clergymen in schools and universities; and the work of church-sponsored social agencies. At present there is no way of estimating the amount and type of counseling done by these various groups, nor is there any information, with the exception of occasional essays, on the problems particular to each. Some of these objectives can be accomplished by a rather simple but detailed program of descriptive research that will set the stage for later explanatory investigation.

Since some of the necessary descriptive studies have broken the ground in some areas of counseling, it is timely for further exploration in these areas, on deeper levels. A crucial area, though difficult to study, is counseling methodology and techniques. It would be valuable, for example, to know more about the comparative effectiveness of non-directive vs. directive counseling, of theological compared with purely interpersonal frameworks. Differing counseling methods might be studied in relation to certain counseling problems, and in relation to personality characteristics of both counselors and counselees.

A related topic of research is the counselor's personality. Some of the variation in counseling can be understood in relation to basic personality factors of ministers-as-counselors. Sheldon and Eleanor Glueck (1956) have pointed to an "X" quality in the "therapeutic personality" which makes some people extremely effective in interpersonal relations, while lack of it almost precludes some from adequate dealings with others. These personality characteristics offer an area of fruitful investigation: studies involving effective versus ineffective counselors (who had comparable training, experience, methodology, and theological perspective) would be a point of departure for such research.

3. *The church as a therapeutic and redemptive "community."* While the churches cannot be isolated, or separated from their clergy, their members, their tradition, their spiritual and temporal values, they can be perceived as communities which can have profound meaning for the health of the individual and of the group as well. This meaning is very intangible and elusive. Membership in the religious group and such formalized religious behavior as church attendance seem to have minor relevance for mental health, as we indicated in an earlier chapter.

The religious institutions—the "churches"—of some primitive groups institutionalize the deviant, the neurotic, even the psychotic, offering him a place to belong, something useful to do. An example is the shaman of some Siberian and Eskimo groups. Does the church in Western society find ways to channelize deviance, or, frozen within the permitted range of its ritual and service, must it reject the deviant for the sake of its own health? What about the marginal individual who lives on the borderland between illness and health; can the church recognize him, and when it does, will it pull him in or push him out?

Some positive and some negative aspects of religious groups are closely related to personality development and mental health. Important factors can be the relationships within the group, the relationships of the group to the wider community, the kind of theological, social, ethical and interpersonal ideas and attitudes that are transmitted, and the way in which they are communicated. Some secondary characteristics which would effect mental health positively or negatively, directly or indirectly, are factors which could be investigated and placed along continua from independence to dependence, from authoritarianism to humanitarianism, from flexibility to rigidity. A positive function of the religious group may be illustrated by analogy to a function seen among the Hutterite sect by Joseph W. Eaton and Robert J. Weil (1955, p. 212): "Hutterite colonies were therapeutic communities in the sense that the traumatic social consequences of being mentally ill were kept at a minimum."

4. *Group experience in the churches.* This increasing movement takes various forms, from the group therapy made available by the church and conducted by a psychiatrist, with no participation by the clergy, to the group-dynamics sessions involving laymen only, or laymen and clergy. An outstanding example of the latter is the Parish Life Conferences of the Episcopal Church. No research has yet been done on the effect of participation in these "intentional" subgroups.

5. *Spiritual healing.* Familiar in one variety in Christian Science, healing is an ancient phenomenon in the churches and is currently becoming more widespread in individual churches of the major denominations, such as the Episcopal and the Presbyterian. Varieties of the movement range from group psychotherapy in a church setting (mentioned above), to the laying on of hands with appropriate prayers.

6. *The smaller sects.* These have been characterized in terms ranging from "fringe groups" to "the third force in Christendom." The hundred or more church groups in this "third force" number over six million members. Revivalist, Pentecostal, Adventist, Fundamentalist, these groups attempt to restore the practices and goals of the early, so-called primitive or sub-apostolic Christian church. Their appeal is so great that they are now one of the fastest-growing

movements on the religious scene. What effect, if any, on mental
health, can be discerned through observation and research on the
uninhibited and exuberant expression of emotion which they encourage, their rigid biblical literalism, their various world views?
What effect do the personality characteristics, the mental health or
non-health of the leaders and members of these groups have on
their religious beliefs, practices, and expression? Is it in such groups
as these that the "marginal" individual can find a spiritual home?

7. The relations between religion and mental health in other than
the Judaeo-Christian groups and traditions, such as Islam, Hinduism,
and Buddhism (with, in the last, particular reference to Zen).

8. The relation between the "private" religious orientation of the
individual and his mental health. This is our major research recommendation. While such a study would be concerned with "religion
and mental health," it would primarily be person-centered. The
emphasis in the present study has been principally on the church and
on the clergyman and his function and role; the emphasis of the
proposed research would be on the church member, and on the non-
member as well; on the religious layman, and on the nonreligious
layman also.

While a range and variety of background and experience would
be desirable among those individuals studied, the approach when
dealing with such unquantifiable factors should not be through a
questionnaire or a battery of tests, but through intensive and extensive depth interviews. All aspects of their religious beliefs, knowledge, sentiments, behavior, and experience would be thoroughly
explored, as well as such related areas as their perception of themselves, of key people in their lives, and of the world in which they
live.

Henry A. Murray, Professor of Clinical Psychology in Harvard
University, holds that if supernatural factors have gradually declined in the belief content of the individual, rather than leaving a
vacuum, they are replaced by other values. This change may occur,
if it occurs at all, not only from childhood to adulthood in the same
individual, but perhaps also from generation to generation. We
would ask: What is the nature of these changes, how are they re-

lated to personality development? What are these "substitute" values and orientations, and, in some instances, activities? Can we discern any effect on the mental health of the individual that may be related to this process?

Gordon W. Allport (1954), Professor of Psychology at Harvard, has distinguished two major typologies in the religion of the individual. The "institutionalized" religious outlook is characterized by reliance on religion to support infantile and magical forms of thinking (e.g., the persistence of the "omnipotence of thought," which was the basis of some of Freud's strongest criticism of religion). The "interiorized" religious orientation on the other hand, is characterized by a comprehensive and guiding view of life, and a turning away from self-centeredness. Fruitful exploration can be carried out in identifying individuals according to these two types (though they are not mutually exclusive), and relating these orientations to such personality variables as authoritarianism, and selected indices of mental health.

The depth interviews that we have suggested as a means of learning about the total religious patterns of the individual, the meaning of religion to him, the ways he translates religious values into life situations, his religious *experience,* in the broad sense of that term, rather than his religious *expression* only—such interviews are limited in scope to an exploration of the past only, and to the edge of the present. More illumination would be gained from long-range developmental studies of the religious changes and growth of individuals, begun early in life and carried on over many years. The clergyman, who often maintains relationships with his parishioners over a long period, would be an ideal resource to enlist in such an endeavor.

The value of knowing the inner religious orientation of the individual at an early stage in his life has been pointed out by Allport (1958), who has expressed the view that adolescence is the period of life—particularly in our society—"when all the relationships between religion and mental health are most raw, exposed, and most accessible." He suggests studying "the extent to which the adolescent's religion both *reflects* and *controls* his modes of handling conflict," and calls attention to some specific problems for exploration that would provide insight into this broad question.

9. *Coordination and communication of research.* Research on the preceding and other topics would be greatly facilitated by the establishment of a center which correlated empirical research material on religion, and coordinated on-going research programs in order to avoid duplication of effort, and to make findings available to interested individuals and institutions, whether representing the churches or the social sciences. Some preliminary steps have been taken by three non-sectarian groups: the Society for the Scientific Study of Religion, the Religious Education Association, and the Academy of Religion and Mental Health. These organizations have made valued contributions, though they do not as yet answer the need for a centralized research communication center.

CONCLUSION

Some clergymen are aware of recent movements in mental health, such as attempts to utilize the total milieu in the treatment of the mentally ill, not only in the widening "therapeutic milieu" of the total hospital setting, but in the community and in the family. Many are sensitive to the need for prevention and for detection of mental health problems. Eaton and Weil (1955, p. 216) point to the need for the long-range cooperation of key institutions:

Preventive mental hygiene would not appear to be a job for piecemeal social action. The home, the school, the place of work, and other social institutions need to work on an integrated long-range program if it is to have a measurable effect. There are no "quickie" techniques in the battle for mental health.

The "observation-exploration-research" orientation we have suggested for the clergy as a philosophy, as an approach to appropriate aspects of their task if not as a formalized activity, may sharpen this awareness and serve to insure that the Church is one of the institutions cooperating fully in the long-range program of prevention.

While a "research orientation" toward his experiences is the main point of our suggestion for the clergyman, the clergy themselves could prove to be a resource for research on religion and mental health. In addition to the long-range program suggested earlier, the clergy have the opportunity for observation of, and participation in, an important learning and growing process. If the individual clergyman, and pastoral counseling centers as well, were to keep good case records, a valuable source of material for the understanding of man, and of human behavior as it is highlighted at times of stress, would be preserved.

The reluctance to keep records or otherwise preserve and, at some future time, make use of the content of counseling derives from the nature of the communication that occurs in the course of pastoral counseling. It is as private, as inviolate, as sacred as that in the confessional itself. So also is that which takes place in the clinic and in the office of the psychiatrist, but significant use has been made of such material without violating the confidence, the integrity, or the anonymity of any individual.

Some might be aghast at the suggestion that the clergyman, the servant of God, should look upon his parishioner as a research subject, as anything but a child of God made in the image of God. Dostoevski has written, "Humane treatment may raise up one in whom the divine image has long been obscured." Often the divine image in man is distorted, cracked, obscured. Finding out the causes of its distortion and obscurity and ways to help the latent image become manifest, and sharing one's increasing insight with others engaged in the same task, may be the most "humane treatment" of all and the most significant task the clergyman can undertake.

References

Allport, G. W., 1954. *The Nature of Prejudice.* Addison-Wesley.

Allport, G. W., 1960. Adolescent religion and mental health: a research approach. In *Religion in the Developing Personality.* Academy of Religion and Mental Health. New York University.

American Hospital Association, *Bulletin,* 1958.

American Hospital Association, *Yearbook,* 1958.

American Medical Association News, 1959, April 20.

American Psychiatric Association, 1957. *List of Fellows and Members of the American Psychiatric Association, 1956–57.*

Andover Newton News Reporter, 1956. III, October.

Angell, R. C., 1951. *The Moral Integration of American Cities.* American Journal of Sociology Monograph. University of Chicago.

Argyle, M., 1959. *Religious Behavior.* Free Press.

Association of Mental Hospital Chaplains, 1957. *Standards for the Mental Hospital Chaplaincy.*

Association of Mental Hospital Chaplains, 1959. *Newsletter, 2,* no. 1.

Bakan, D., 1958. *Sigmund Freud and the Jewish Mystical Tradition.* Van Nostrand.

Baron, S., 1937. Jewish emancipation. In *Encyclopedia of the Social Sciences,* Vol. 8. Macmillan.

Barron, F., 1954. *Personal Soundness in University Graduate Students.* University of California (Berkeley).

Barton, W. E., 1959. Personal communication.

Bay, A. P., 1956. Foreword. In I. Belknap, *Human Problems of a State Mental Hospital.* McGraw-Hill.

Becker, A. H., 1958. The function of relationship in pastoral counseling. Unpublished doctoral dissertation. Boston University.

Bier, W. C., 1958. In *Some Considerations of Early Attempts in Cooperation Between Religion and Psychiatry.* Group for the Advancement of Psychiatry.

Bier, W. C., and Schneiders, A. A. (Eds.), 1958. *Proceedings of the Second*

Institute for the Clergy on Problems in Pastoral Psychology. Fordham University, Department of Psychiatry.

Blizzard, S., 1956. The minister's dilemma. *Christ. Cent., 73,* 508.

Blumen, J. L. and Eister, A. W., 1958. Role-expectations of American clergymen and of non-professional social workers with reference to "pastoral counseling." Paper presented at 16th meeting of the Society for the Scientific Study of Religion.

Blumen, J. L., and Eister, A. W., 1959. Conseillers confessionels et conseillers professionels autour de la psychologie pastorale. *Arch. de Sociol. des Relig.,* janvier-juin, 131.

Boisen, A. T., 1948a. The minister as counsellor. *J. Pastoral Care,* Spring, 13.

Boisen, A. T., 1948b. The service of worship in a mental hospital: its therapeutic significance. *J. Pastoral Care,* Spring, 1.

Boisen, A. T., 1954. Group therapy: the Elgin plan. *Pastoral Psychol.,* March, 33.

Boisen, A. T., 1959. Personal communication.

Boston University Counseling Center, 1957. *Annual Report.*

Bruder, E. E., 1953a. Clinical pastoral training as a hospital medium in public relations. *Pastoral Psychol.,* November, 27.

Bruder, E. E., 1953b. The role of the chaplain in patient relationships: initial religious interview. *J. Pastoral Care,* Spring, 37.

Bruder, E. E., 1953c. Some theological considerations in clinical pastoral education. Paper presented at Fourth Annual National Conference on Clinical Pastoral Training. *J. Pastoral Care, 8,* no. 3.

Bruder, E. E., 1957. Training the mental hospital chaplain. *J. Pastoral Care, 8,* no. 3.

Bruder, E. E., 1958. Administrative concerns in a public mental hospital program. Paper presented at meeting of Association of Mental Hospital Chaplains. Academy of Religion and Mental Health.

Bruder, E. E. and Barb, Marian, 1956. A survey of ten years of clinical pastoral training at Saint Elizabeths Hospital. U.S. Dept. Health, Educ., and Welfare, St. Elizabeths Hospital, Chaplain Services Branch.

Bryan, D. C., 1957. The institute of religion. *Perkins School of Theology Journal, X,* no. 2.

Campbell, E. and Pettigrew, T., 1959. *Christians in Racial Crisis.* Public Affairs Press.

Carlin, J. E. and Mendlovitz, S. H., 1958. The American rabbi. In M. Sklare (Ed.), *The Jews: Social Patterns of an American Group.* Free Press.

Carpenter, C., 1945. Suggestions from the war fronts on the needs of pastoral care we must meet. In S. Hiltner (Ed.), *Clinical Pastoral Training.* Federal Council of Churches, Commission on Religion and Health.

Cassian, J., 1894. (Cassianus, Johannes). Works: translated with prolegomena, prefaces, and notes by E. C. S. Gibson. In P. Schaff (Ed.), *A Select Library of the Nicene and Post-Nicene Fathers,* 2nd series, vol. 11.

Catholic Directory: Almanac and Clergy List, 1959. Witzius.

Caudill, W. A., 1958. *The Psychiatric Hospital as a Small Society.* Harvard University Press.

Cayton, H. and Nishi, S. M., 1955. *The Changing Scene. Churches and Social Welfare,* vol. II. National Council of the Churches of Christ in the U.S.A.

Deitchman, R. B. The evolution of a ministerial counseling center. *J. Pastoral Care, 11,* 207.

Dittes, J., 1959. Personal communication.

Donovan, J. D., 1951. The Catholic priest: a study in the sociology of the professions. Unpublished doctoral dissertation. Harvard University.

Eaton, J. W. and Weil, R. J., 1955. *Culture and Mental Disorders.* Free Press.

Edwards, J., 1746. *The Treatise on the Religious Affections.*

Frumkin, R. M., 1955. Occupation and major mental disorders. In A. M. Rose (Ed.), *Mental Health and Mental Disorder: A Sociological Approach.* Norton.

Galdston, I., 1957. Review: A. T. Boisen, *Religion in Crisis and Custom. Ment. Hyg., 41:*146.

Glueck, S. and Glueck, Eleanor, 1956. *Physique and Delinquency.* Harper.

Gross, L., 1959. *God and Freud.* McKay.

Gurin, G., Veroff, J., and Feld, Sheila, 1960. *Americans View Their Mental Health.* Basic Books.

Hathorne, B. C., 1960. A critical analysis of Protestant church counseling centers. Unpublished Th.D. dissertation. Boston University.

Herr, V. V., 1958. Personal communication.

Hiltner, S. (Ed.), 1945a. *Clinical Pastoral Training.* Report on the 1944 National Conference on Clinical Training in Theological Education. Federal Council of Churches of Christ in America, Commission on Religion and Health.

Hiltner, S., 1945b. The development of the clinical training movement as a whole. In S. Hiltner (Ed.), *Clinical Pastoral Training.* Federal Council of Churches of Christ in America, Commission on Religion and Health.

Hiltner, S., 1958. *Preface to Pastoral Theology.* Abingdon.

Hiltner, S., 1959. The Christian shepherd. *Pastoral Psychol.,* March, 53.

Hofmann, H., 1959. Personal communication.

Hollander, I. F., 1959. Personal communication.

Hollingshead, A. B. and Redlich, F. C., 1958. *Social Class and Mental Illness: A Community Study.* Wiley.

Howe, R., 1945. The development of the clinical training movement through the Philadelphia Divinity School. In S. Hiltner (Ed.), *Clinical Pastoral*

Training. Federal Council of Churches of Christ in America, Commission on Religion and Health.

Hunter, D. R., 1945. The development of the clinical training movement through the New England Group. In S. Hiltner (Ed.), *Clinical Pastoral Training*. Federal Council of Churches of Christ in America, Commission on Religion and Health.

Institute of Pastoral Care, 1957. *Summer Schools of Pastoral Care.*

Jahoda, Marie, 1958. *Current Concepts of Positive Mental Health*. Basic Books.

James, W., 1902. *The Varieties of Religious Experience.*

Jammes, J. M., 1955. The social role of the priest. *Am. Cath. Sociol. Rev., 15,* 94.

Johnson, P. E., 1947. Methods of pastoral counseling. *J. Pastoral Care, 1,* no. 1.

Johnson, P. E., 1955. The pastor as counselor. *Ann. N.Y. Acad. Sci., 63,* 423.

Journal of Pastoral Care, 1957. Editorial. Summer, 106.

Kagan, H. E., 1955. Our prayers—a psychological reinterpretation. Address to 43rd General Assembly, Union of American Hebrew Congregations.

Kagan, H. E., 1959. Personal communication.

Kegley, C. W. and Bretall, R. W. (Eds.), 1952. *The Theology of Paul Tillich.* Macmillan.

Keidel, K. W., 1957. A chaplain looks at his patients, *J. Pastoral Care.* Summer, 98.

Klink, T. W., 1958. The chaplain and the acutely disturbed patient. *J. Pastoral Care.* Fall, 137.

Landis, B. Y. (Ed.), 1957. *Yearbook of American Churches.* National Council of Churches of Christ in the U.S.A.

Lerner, M., 1957. *American as a Civilization.* Simon & Schuster.

Leslie, R. C., 1956. The goals of clinical pastoral education. Fifth National Conference on Clinical Pastoral Education.

Linn, L., 1955. The chaplain. In *A Handbook of Hospital Psychiatry*. International Universities Press.

Loomis, E., Jr., 1957. Course announcement. Union Theological Seminary.

Loomis, E., Jr. Personal communication.

Mailloux, N., 1956. In *Working relationships between pastor and psychiatrist.* Third Annual Series of Pastoral Psychology Workshops. St. John's University, Institute for Mental Health.

Maryland, State of, 1957. Report of legislative committee for the study of mental hospitals.

May, R., Angel, E., and Ellenberger, H., 1958. *Existence.* Basic Books.

McDonnel, K., 1957. Psychiatry and pastoral psychology: the experience of an "Institute for Mental Health." *Lumen Vitae XII,* no. 2. International Center for Studies in Religious Education (Brussels).

McNeill, J. T., 1951. *A History of the Cure of Souls.* Harper.

Menninger Foundation, 1957. *Report of progress, 1956–57.*

Meserve, H. C., 1958. *No Peace of Mind.* Harcourt, Brace.

Myers, J. K. and Roberts, B. H., 1958. Some relations between religion, ethnic origin, and mental illness. In M. Sklare (Ed.), *The Jews: Social Patterns of an American Group.* Free Press.

Nameche, G. F., 1958. Pastoral counseling in Protestant churches. Part. I: the minister as counselor. Unpublished manuscript.

Nameche, G. F., 1959. Pastoral counseling in Protestant churches. Part II: the parish counselee. Unpublished manuscript.

National Conference on Clinical Pastoral Training, 1953. Report. (Mimeographed.)

National Council of Churches of Christ in the U.S.A., Dept of Pastoral Services, 1958. Opportunities for study, training, and experience in pastoral psychology—1958. *Pastoral Psychol.,* January, 17.

National Health Education Committee, 1959. *Facts on the major killing and crippling diseases in the United States today.*

Niebuhr, H. R. (in collaboration with D. D. Williams and J. M. Gustafson), 1956. *The Purpose of the Church and Its Ministry.* Harper.

Niebuhr, H. R. *et al.,* 1956. Theological education in America. Bulletin *No. 5,* April.

Niebuhr, H. R., Williams, D. D. and Gustafson, J. M., 1957. *The Advancement of Theological Education.* Harper.

Plunkett, R. J. and Gordon, J. E., 1960. *Epidemiology and Mental Illness.* Basic Books.

Religious Education Association, 1960. Proposals for research. *Relig. Educ.,* Jan.-Feb., 47.

Roberts, A. and Donaldson, J. (Eds.), 1951. *The Ante-Nicene Fathers.* Translation of the writings of the Fathers down to A.D. 325, Vol. 7. Eerdmans.

Roberts, A. and Donaldson, J. (Eds.), 1956. *The Nicene and Post-Nicene Fathers,* Vol. 13. Eerdmans.

Robinson, R., DeMarche, D. F. and Wagle, Mildred K., 1960. *Community Resources in Mental Health.* Basic Books.

Schnitzer, J., 1958. Rabbis and counseling: report on a project. *Jewish Social Studies, 20,* no. 3.

Shipley, D. C. *et al.,* 1957. Clinical pastoral education and the task of theology. Symposium. *Perkins School of Theology Journal, 10,* no. 2.

Sklare, M. (Ed.), 1958. *The Jews: Social Patterns of an American Group.* Free Press.

Smith, L. M., 1958. Parish clergymen's role images as pastoral counselors. Paper read at meeting of Society for the Scientific Study of Religion.

Smith, M. B., 1959. Research strategies toward a conception of positive mental health. *Amer. Psychol., 14,* 673.

Solomon, H., 1959. Unpublished address.

Soloveitchik, J. B., 1958. Personal communication.

Stanton, A. H. and Schwartz, M. S., 1954. *The Mental Hospital*. Basic Books.

Sullivan, W., 1959a. Unpublished address.

Sullivan, W., 1959b. Personal communication.

Thorndike, E. L., 1939. American cities and states. In *Ann. N.Y. Acad. Sci.*, *39*, 213.

Tillich, P., 1948. *The Protestant Era*. University of Chicago.

U.S. Dept. of Commerce, Bureau of the Census, 1957. *Statistical Abstract of the United States*. Government Printing Office.

Weigel, G., 1959. Challenge of peace. *Pastoral Psychol.*, February, 31.

Weir, E., 1941. *Criminology: A Scientific Study*. Institute for the Scientific Study of Crime.

Wolf, R. C., 1958. Religious trends in the United States. *Christianity Today*, *3*, 3.

Wolff, H. G., 1959. Presentation by Dr. Wolff. In *Religion, Science, and Mental Health*. Symposium, Academy of Religion and Mental Health. New York University.

Appendix I

Pastoral Counseling Centers

California

1. Pastoral Counseling Service, Pacific School of Religion, 1798 Scenic Avenue, Berkeley. Professor Robert C. Leslie, Ph.D.
2. Church Welfare Bureau of the Church Federation of Los Angeles, 3330 West Adams Boulevard, Los Angeles. Mrs. Frances Poynter, M.S.W., Director, Consultation and Counseling Services.
3. The Counseling Center, First Congregational Church, 535 South Hoover, Los Angeles. Mr. Clarence E. Stubert, Director.
4. Department of Counseling, Los Angeles Baptist City Mission Society, Suite 701, 427 West 5th Street, Los Angeles. The Rev. Carroll Wright, Th.D., Director.
5. First Methodist Church of Los Angeles, Church Service Bureau, Counseling Center, 813 South Hope Street, Los Angeles. The Rev. J. Richard Sneed, Director.
6. Mental Health Clinic of the Westwood Community Methodist Church, 10497 Wilshire Boulevard, Los Angeles. Harvey Strassman, M.D., Director.
7. Mental Health Clinic, St. Matthew's Lutheran Church, 11031 Camarillo Street, North Hollywood. Jack A. Jurasky, M.D., Director.
8. Department of Counseling, Palos Verdes Peninsula Council of Churches, 415 Paseo Del Mar, Palos Verdes Estates. Rev. Lester Kim, Ph.D., Director.
9. Pastoral Counseling Center of the First Methodist Church, 500 East Colorado Street, Pasadena. Rev. Howard Clinebell, Ph.D., Director.
10. Church Counseling Service, 841 Woodside Road, Redwood City. The Rev. Paul S. Kurtz, Executive Director.
11. Pastoral Counseling Center of the First Christian Church of Whittier, 301 North Greenleaf, Whittier. Rev. James Laughrun, Director.

Colorado

12. Social Service Department, Denver Area Council of Churches, 300 Trinity Building, 1830 Broadway, Denver. The Rev. Dale Dargitz, Director.

Florida

13. Religio-Psychiatric Clinic, First Presbyterian Church, Hollywood. Elbert McLaury, M.D., Director.
14. Central Florida Counseling Center, 320 North Main Street, Orlando. The Rev. Russell L. Dicks, D.D., Director.

Illinois

15. Youth Service Bureau, Church Federation of Greater Chicago, Room 1322, 127 No. Dearborn Street, Chicago. Mr. Walter G. Rest, Director.
16. Minister of Pastoral Care, Glenview Community Church, 1000 Elm Street, Glenview.

Indiana

17. Pastoral Care and Counseling Center, Central Methodist Church, 300 Mary Street, Evansville. The Rev. William N. Burton, Director.
18. Pastoral Care and Counseling Center, Wesley Hall, 326 East Wayne Street, Fort Wayne. The Rev. Bryant J. Howard, Director.
19. Pastoral Care and Counseling Center, City Methodist Church, 575 Washington Street, Gary. The Rev. Glen F. Hulbert, Director.
20. Christian Counseling Center, First Methodist Church, Hammond. The Rev. Eugene Balsley, Director.
21. Pastoral Care and Counseling, Indiana Area of The Methodist Church, 324 Chamber of Commerce Building, Indianapolis. The Rev. James E. Doty, Ph.D., Director.
22. Patsoral Care and Counseling Center, North Methodist Church, 3808 North Meridian Street, Indianapolis. The Rev. Kenneth E. Reed, Director.
23. Pastoral Care and Counseling Center, Wall Street Methodist Church, Wall Street at Chestnut, Jeffersonville. The Rev. Alda I. Carter, Director.
24. Southern Indiana Personal Counseling Service, 231 East Market Street, Jeffersonville. The Rev. H. Rea Gray, Counselor.
25. Pastoral Care and Counseling Center, High Street Methodist Church, High and Adams Street, Muncie. The Rev. Harold D. Neel, D.D., Director.

Iowa

26. Personal Problems Clinic, First Baptist Church, Court at First Street, Ottumwa. The Rev. Charles A. Thunn, Director.

Kansas

27. Methodist Counseling Center, First Methodist Church, 88th and Jefferson, Junction City. The Rev. J. Lester McGee, D.D., Director.

Kentucky

28. The Family Relations Center, 624 South Floyd Street, Louisville. The Rev. John H. Boyle, Director.
29. The Counseling Service, Southern Baptist Theological Seminary, 2825 Lexington Road, Louisville. Professor Wayne E. Oates, Th.D., Director.

Maine

30. Pastoral Counseling Service, Orono Methodist Church, 38 Oak Street, Orono. The Rev. Robert E. Allten.

Maryland

31. Community Counseling, Grace Methodist Church, 7001 New Hampshire Avenue, Takoma Park. Milo F. Benningfield, M.A., Director.

Massachusetts

32. Pastoral Counseling Service, Boston University School of Theology, 745 Commonwealth Avenue, Boston. The Rev. Paul E. Johnson, Ph.D., Director.
33. Old South Congregational Church, 645 Boylston Street, Boston. The Rev. John M. Billinsky, Ed.D., Counselor, and Associate to the Ministers.
34. Marriage Counseling Service and Group Psychotherapy Program, Community Church of Boston, 565 Boylston Street, Boston. The Rev. Donald G. Lothrop, Director.
35. Personal Counseling Service, First Baptist Church, 5 Magazine Street, Cambridge. The Rev. Lynn C. Smith, Director.
36. Pastoral Counseling Center, Cape Cod Council of Churches, First Baptist Church, Main Street, Hyannis. The Rev. Wallen L. Bean, Coordinator.
37. Pastoral Counseling Center, First Methodist Church, City Hall Square, Lynn. The Rev. Ralph H. Manwiller, Director.
38. John Eliot Counseling Center, Eliot Congregational Church, 474 Center Street, Newton. The Rev. William Clark, Counselor.
39. Pastoral Counseling Center, Springfield Council of Churches, 154 Sumner Avenue, Springfield. The Rev. John A. Caswell, Director.
40. Pastoral Counseling Center, Wesley Methodist Church, Main and State Streets, Worcester. The Rev. James R. Uhlinger, D.D., Director.
41. Counseling Center of Worcester, Greater Worcester Council of Churches, 63 Wachusett Street, Worcester. The Rev. John I. Smith, Director.

Michigan

42. The Counseling Service, The Merrill-Palmer School, 71 East Ferry, Detroit. The Rev. Aaron L. Rutledge, Th.D., Director.
43. Religious Counseling Center Church, 5055 Plainfield Avenue, N.E., Grand Rapids. The Rev. H. Walter Yoder, Director.

Minnesota

44. Wesley Methodist Church Counseling Center, Marquette at Grant St., Minneapolis. The Rev. John B. Oman, D.D., Director.

Missouri

45. Mid-West Christian Counseling Center, 208 Tower Building, 116 West 47th Street, Kansas City. The Rev. R. Lofton Hudson, Ph.D., Director.
46. Counseling Center, Central Presbyterian Church, 3501 Campbell Street, Kansas City. The Rev. Frederick H. Olert, D.D., Director.
47. Cathedral Counseling Center, Christ Church Cathedral, 1210 Locust Street, St. Louis. The Rev. Allan N. Zacher, Jr., Director.
48. Ministerial Counseling Center, Metropolitan Church Federation, Pilgrim Congregational Church, 826 North Union Boulevard, St. Louis. The Rev. Allen Hackett, Director.
49. Marriage Counseling Service, Greene County Guidance Clinic, 1722½ North Robberson, Springfield. Donald Ballie, Executive Secretary.

New Hampshire

50. Diocesan Counseling Service, 63 Green Street, Concord. The Rev. William H. Crouch, Director.

New Jersey

51. Lutheran Welfare Association of New Jersey, 93 Nelson Avenue, Jersey City. The Rev. Carl Futchs, D.D., Executive Secretary.

New York

52. Pastoral Counseling Center, Trinity Methodist Church, 711 Niagara Falls Boulevard, Buffalo. The Rev. Foster J. Williams, Ph.D., Director.
53. Counseling Service, Asbury-Delaware Methodist Church, 80 West Tupper Street, Buffalo. The Rev. Dean E. Richardson, Director.
54. The American Foundation of Religion and Psychiatry, 3 West 29th Street, New York. Smiley Blanton, M.D., Director.

North Carolina

55. Counseling Program, Myers Park Baptist Church, 1900 Queens Road, Charlotte. The Rev. W. Emory Trainham, Jr., Director.

56. Out-Patient Counseling Service, Department of Pastoral Care, North Carolina Baptist Hospital, Winston-Salem. The Rev. Richard K. Young, Th.D., Director.
57. Counseling Service, R. J. Reynolds Tobacco Company, Reynolds Building, Winston-Salem. The Rev. Clifford H. Peace, Counselor.

Ohio

58. Christ Episcopal Church Counseling Service, 318 East 4th Street, Cincinnati. The Rev. Morris F. Arnold, Rector.
59. Counseling Center of Trinity Cathedral, Euclid and East 22nd Street, Cleveland. The Rev. David Loegled, Dean.
60. Cleveland Counseling Center, 11311 Shaker Boulevard, Cleveland. The Rev. Warren W. Bentzinger, D.D., Director.
61. The Counseling Department, First Community Church, Columbus. The Rev. Robert A. Blees, Minister of Counseling.

Pennsylvania

62. Pastoral Counseling Service of the Religious Department of the Presbyterian Hospital in Philadelphia, 51 North 39th Street, Philadelphia. The Rev. Robert G. Foulkes, S.T.D., Chaplain, Director.

Rhode Island

63. Counseling Program, Calvary Baptist Church, 747 Broad Street, Providence. The Rev. John G. Koehler, Pastor-Director.

South Carolina

64. Central Methodist Church Counseling Service, 223 West Cheves Street, Florence. The Rev. Wilson S. Lambert, Minister for Counseling.

Tennessee

65. Pastoral Counseling Service, Second Presbyterian Church, Knoxville. The Rev. William E. Crane, Th.D., Counseling Pastor.
66. Counseling Center, First Methodist Church, Locust and Clinch Streets, Knoxville. The Rev. Keith McCord, Minister of Pastoral Care and Counseling.

Texas

67. Baptist Marriage and Family Counseling Center, Price Hall, Suite 101, Southwestern Baptist Theological Seminary, Fort Worth 15. The Rev. John W. Drakeford, Director.
68. Family Counseling Service, The Institute of Religion, Jesse H. Jones

Library Building, Texas Medical Center, Houston. The Rev. Joseph Knowles, Th.D., Director.

69. Pastoral Counseling Service, Trinity Baptist Church, 319 East Mulberry, San Antonio. The Rev. B. David Edens, Ed.D., Counseling Minister.

Virginia

70. Southside Area Family Counseling Service, 136 South Sycamore Street, Petersburg. Mrs. Frank S. Moore, Executive Director.

Washington, D.C.

71. Counseling Service, Lutheran Inner Mission Society, 2633 Sixteenth Street, N.W. The Rev. Paul M. Orso, Ph.D., Director.

72. The Pastoral Institute, 3000 Connecticut Avenue, N.W. The Rev. Knox Kreutzer, Executive Director.

73. Foundry Counseling Service, 1500 Sixteenth Street, N.W. The Rev. Berkley C. Hathorne, Th.D., Director.

Joint Commission
on Mental Illness and Health

PARTICIPATING AGENCIES

American Academy of Neurology
American Academy of Pediatrics
American Association for the Advancement of Science
American Association on Mental Deficiency
American Association of Psychiatric Clinics for Children
American College of Chest Physicians
American Hospital Association
American Legion
American Medical Association
American Nurses Association and The National League for Nursing (Coordinating Council of)
American Occupational Therapy Association
American Orthopsychiatric Association
American Personnel and Guidance Association
American Psychiatric Association
American Psychoanalytic Association
American Psychological Association

American Public Health Association
American Public Welfare Association
Association for Physical and Mental Rehabilitation
Association of American Medical Colleges
Association of State and Territorial Health Officers
Catholic Hospital Association
Central Inspection Board, American Psychiatric Association
Children's Bureau, Department of Health, Education, and Welfare
Council of State Governments
Department of Defense, U.S.A.
National Association for Mental Health
National Association of Social Workers
National Committee Against Mental Illness
National Education Association
National Institute of Mental Health
National Medical Association
National Rehabilitation Association

Office of Vocational Rehabilitation, Department of Health, Education, and Welfare

United States Department of Justice Veterans Administration

INDIVIDUAL MEMBERS

Kenneth E. Appel, M.D.
Philadelphia, Pa.
Walter H. Baer, M.D.
Peoria, Illinois
Leo H. Bartemeier, M.D.
Baltimore, Maryland
Walter E. Barton, M.D.
Boston, Massachusetts
Otto L. Bettag, M.D.
Springfield, Illinois
Mr. George Bingaman
Purcell, Oklahoma
Francis J. Braceland, M.D.
Hartford, Connecticut
Hugh T. Carmichael, M.D.
Chicago, Illinois
J. Frank Casey, M.D.
Washington, D.C.
James M. Cunningham, M.D.
Dayton, Ohio
John E. Davis, Sc.D.
Rehoboth Beach, Delaware
Neil A. Dayton, M.D.
Mansfield Depot, Connecticut
Miss Loula Dunn
Chicago, Illinois
Howard D. Fabing, M.D.
Cincinnati, Ohio
Very Rev. Msgr. P. J. Frawley, Ph.D.
New York, New York
Mr. Mike Gorman
Washington, D.C.
Robert T. Hewitt, M.D.
Bethesda, Maryland
Herman E. Hilleboe, M.D.
Albany, New York

Nicholas Hobbs, Ph.D.
Nashville, Tennessee
Bartholomew W. Hogan, Rear
Admiral, M.C., U.S.N.,
Washington, D.C.
Louis Jacobs, M.D.
Washington, D.C.
Miss Adaline Johnesse,
Washington, D.C.
M. Ralph Kaufman, M.D.
New York, New York
William S. Langford, M.D.
New York, New York
Miss Madeleine Lay
New York, New York
Mary F. Liston, R.N.
New York, New York
Jack Masur, M.D.
Bethesda, Maryland
Berwyn F. Mattison, M.D.
New York, New York
Ernst Mayr, Ph.D.
Cambridge, Massachusetts
Robert T. Morse, M.D.
Washington, D.C.
Ralph H. Ojemann, Ph.D.
Iowa City, Iowa
Winfred Overholser, M.D.
Washington, D.C.
Howard W. Potter, M.D.
Thiells, New York
Mathew Ross, M.D.
Washington, D.C.
Mr. Charles Schlaifer
New York, New York

Consultant in Social Sciences: Gordon W. Blackwell, Ph.D.
  Tallahassee, Florida
Consultant in Epidemiology: John E. Gordon, M.D.
  Boston, Massachusetts
Associate Director for Administration: Richard J. Plunkett, M.D. (deceased)
  Boston, Massachusetts
Associate Director and Consultant on Law: Charles S. Brewton, LL.B.
  Alexandria, Virginia
Librarian: Mary R. Strovink
  Boston, Massachusetts

Index